CLAYDON

© Hubert Chapman 1991

Published by Brundall Books
39 St. Lawrence Avenue
Brundall, Norwich, Norfolk

Printed by Thornton and Pearson Limited
Bradford, West Yorkshire

Designed by Tadpole Graphics

ISBN 0 9518217 0 9

CLAYDON
Hubert Chapman

Brundall Books

FOREWORD

The life, ways and occurrences shown in the accounts put together here lay entirely in the first years of the astonishing century which is now nearing its end.

They were the years of my boyhood, the beginnings of a long life which has seen changes in village life unimaginable in the eager mind I seem to have been born with just as Edward VII came to the throne.

It was soon said in Claydon that I had eyes and ears for everything. Because of this, perhaps, my North Buckinghamshire village people and their surroundings are registered very clearly in my memory, enabling me to present some of them and their doings almost exactly as they were. The places and people described in these stories are all real places and people of the early twentieth century. Most of the events related here actually took place, though here and there imagination has been used to supplement the bare bones of village narrative and, occasionally, names have been altered.

The great changes that were imminent and even upon us by the time of the 1914-18 war have put those early days in sharp contrast so that for me a bright clear light shines upon them to this day.

I am grateful to my son Robin Chapman and my daughter Gillian Spencer who helped me prepare these stories for publication.

Hubert Chapman   1991

CLAYDON

Four Claydon villages lay on the belt of clay north of the Chiltern Hills in the Vale of Aylesbury. Here and there the clay rose in rounded ridges. Three of the villages sat, or partly sat, on two of them. All had their roots in countryside where the soil grew food for dairy herds and heavy crops of corn and roots in fields on farms with distinct and separate characters. No farms or fields, were extensive, most had a feel of cosiness in them, of neighbourliness, homeliness.

Untarred roads ambled to Aylesbury, Buckingham and to Winslow, the small market-town, between hedges of thorn, wild crab, brambles and dog-roses, shaded by elms and oaks and an occasional ash, whose girth and spread spoke of the strength of the soil.

Steeple Claydon, lying off from the other villages, crowned one rise and then dropped to its foot. It boasted the largest population of the four, five hundred or so people. It had the only church with a spire, St. Michael's, also a police-station, with a resident police-sergeant and a lock-up for the encouragement of order and sobriety in the district, while possessing several licensed inns threatening both.

Middle Claydon, much the smallest community, was the estate village once common to manor-houses with parks. Its main residents dwelt beyond the park pale, most near the North Lodge. They spent their days, years and some their lives serving the house-people in estate forestry and management, in working the estate farm, in the laundry and repair-shops and stores in the courtyard, others under the manor roof with a butler and a house-keeper in dual charge there.

The aged, white-haired, squire lived quietly in Claydon House in the middle of the park, his vigorous busy lady less quietly there. They had inherited a South as well as the North Lodge, an avenue of trees, for approach on important occasions, and a front view of two lakes and tree-cover spread out below them. The house had a wide gravelled frontage on which cannons had been fired at Queen Victoria's Diamond Jubilee in 1897. On the south side was a spacious lawn, discreetly shaded, where they, the people of the villages and visitors from afar gathered to be entertained on occasions such as that and for momentous ones like the coming-of-age of an heir, the family weddings and the christening of an heir.

The parish church, All Saints', stood a few paces from their threshold. It was in the proper ordering of things that the rector himself and his congregation must cross the park for worship, nuptials, christenings, churchings and burials, just as it had been usual in the previous generation for that squire's sister to be the wife of the rector of the time and so his assistant supervisor of the villagers' lives over the four villages.

Hence, a chant, remembered but no longer sung with the original wry feeling: 'Thank you, mum, for the britches, mum, you give me for me husband, mum. We went to church a-Sunday, mum, and heard a very good sermon, mum' — and the assertion by villagers who dwelt on past times that the good lady kept scissors in a reticule for the removal of decoration from frivolous maidens' hats.

On the hill which ran north and south, overlooking the higher Quainton Hills, was East Claydon, settled comfortably on its northern end, right at the brow St. Mary's Church, its square tower a landmark. Next to it was the White House, old and rambling behind a high wall of aged brick, where, sometimes in the past, the estate heir lived awaiting his inheritance, in these later times Arthur Bryant, historian and village cricketer.

Spreading south along the length of the hill were then the schools, old and new, the village hall and library, square Botolph House with its huge cedar before it, the thatched post-office, the smithy, the wheel-wright's and carpenter's shops, Webbs' General Store, thatch and timber and red-brick cottages, farm-yards, stack-yards and clumps of elms, Botolph Claydon. Old cartographers called it Claydon St. Botolph with little warranty. Ancient Botyl, used by most natives, was probably better.

Prominent near its southern end a single elm towered over the cross-roads reached as you climbed from the valley, the Cross Tree. It stood at a sort of gathering-place with an open area of grass and roadway before it, under it an oak seat shiny from use.

No more than a few hundred yards onwards the hill ended, though beyond it again there began another rise covered by oak-woods, the remnants of Bernwood Forest. From a point there, looking South-West on a clear day, might be seen the glint of distant spires and towers, the city of Oxford, less than twenty miles away.

The village did not quite end at the Cross Tree, more dwellings, cottages and a small farm-stead stood westward beside the road which dipped towards Middle Claydon and at the tree Weir Lane began a small run south. It fell a little and then ran, closely skirting the Weir Pond, L-shaped and large, to pass on its left, and standing on a high bank, a one-time farm-house of timber-frame and thatch, its windows looking directly over the ever-changing water, where distant cattle drank, moor-hens scooted and Aylesbury ducks quacked.

Beyond the pond, on ground rising again, were the granary, wagon-sheds, stables, rolling paddock, court-yard and dairy of Bernwood Farm. The brick-built house stood tall and imposing behind a screen of firs. Boldly it marked the end of human habitation, just as St. Mary's Church ended all at the hill's East Claydon end. Approached from the east, and rising to it whatever the approach, the whole extent made a striking silhouette against a westering sun and cloudless evening sky. An ordnance-survey bench-mark made Bernwood farm-house three hundred and one feet above sea-level, another made St. Mary's church one foot lower. The two villages, almost conjoined, together comprised about that same number of people, three hundred.

The house beside the pond had been a farm-house for more than two hundred years, but when Bernwood Farm was built and fashioned to include its acreages, in the 1860's, it was divided into two cottages. As it was L-shaped like the pond, one looked down the greater length of the water, while the other stood sideways to it. Rambling, with passages, two parlours, two kitchens with coppers, one with a bread-oven, four or five bedrooms and two stair-cases it divided comfortably.

Behind it, across an area of cobbled yard and grass possessing a covered well and pump, the separate brick-built dairy became a third cottage and so, with the Bernwood Farm people close, all who lived adjacent to the pond became 'them at the Weir', without question.

They valued their separation, though the jigging,

skipping smugness of the young members about this was scornfully rejected in the school play-grounds. The Weir people stood together and were uniquely placed. Witness the landscape artist who set up on the paddock for a view along the lane, something like Constable's *Hay Wain* — team-horses drinking after a hard day at plough, the farm-dogs at their heels, or the carters riding them into the pond with huge splashings, to clean their fetlocks and hooves. The same earnest man arrived in succeeding summers, was more or less expected.

Photographers fixed tripods in the lane and from their work post-card views proliferated: 'A Glimpse of Rural Bucks', 'The Hay-Wagon Trundles Home', 'The Weir, Claydon St. Botolph', 'Timber and Thatch and Plough-horses drinking'. These travelled the country. A green half-penny stamp with King Edward the Seventh's head on it assured passage in all directions in the heyday of the picture-postcard.

At the turn of the new century the two cottages which faced the pond fell vacant together and, by further coincidence, the new-comers were bridal pairs. The home with the tile-capped bulge on its outer wall, the bread-oven, welcomed Ada Jennings of the village and Harry Blindell, a gentlemen's tailor, from Ware in Hertfordshire, who set up house-keeping and business at once.

The other cottage stood waiting while George James Chapman — 'bachelor of this Parish of East Claydon' — borrowed for the day Emily, the chestnut pony, and the light trap from Bernwood Farm to drive to Brackley, fifteen miles away and just inside Northamptonshire, for his wedding to Sarah Susanna, otherwise Sally Wright of Juniper Hill. The wedding and celebrations over there was then the ride back to Claydon. Unknown to them as they bowled along a village reception was in hand. The bride-groom played the baritone-horn in the village band. His small group of fellow-bandsmen lay in wait on the grass bank before the open front doorway of the cottage, which, being a country one, was at the side; so they stood hidden in the angle of the house, while neighbours and friends, armed with rice and confetti, chatted and laughed in the lane, all dancingly reflected in the wavelets of the pond. It was to be a surprise welcome. The band would strike up at the moment of arrival with a polka.

Emily brought the trap along at a spanking trot heading for home. She made nothing of the rise into the village, tossed her head at the outburst of cheers at the Cross Tree and turned into Weir Lane in her best style as her passengers rose for the anticipated first cup of tea amidst their new furnishings in their own front-room. The signal given by the watchers at the Cross Tree at the sound of pounding feet in the wake of the trap, Jackie, the band-master, raised his cornet. 'Ready men', he said, 'I shall count to three — give them your all'. He grinned broadly and placed the mouth-piece to his lips. Eyes shone, instruments shone at the ready, every man drew breath, even Jimmy the drummer, as the chatterers in the lane made way, clapping and laughing and Emily came to a stand.

Bride and groom stood for a second of complete astonishment when Jackie gave a brisk, 'One-two-three' and the band gave them their all in a joyful opening blast accompanied by loud cheers, hurrays and laughter. Stinging rice and showers of confetti found their mark, hats were tossed in air and the farm-dogs came bounding to the scene barking furiously.

It was all too much for Emily. She reared in her shafts, then veered as if to return to Juniper Hill. The groom, dead against this, gave a mighty haul on the reins which brought her round to be pulled up, plunging, stamping and protesting, only avoiding the drenching of his bride by the width of a wheel's rim.

The band moaned to silence, the spectators cried: 'Mercy on us!' and Sally leapt to the road. No longer a beaming and blushing bride, and far from being carried over the threshold, she stumped over it, deploring in strong words 'the whole show'.

Emily stood trembling and George descended to the road in a great hush, broken at last by Jackie, saying, 'Oh dear — could ha' been worse, though, George' and George said, 'Thanks, men — it's the thought that counts. She'll come round. I'd better go in'.

After parley and assurance that Emily was soothed and safely stabled, while declaring her the only innocent in all this besides herself, Sally was persuaded to stand at the threshold for the polka, which, after all, was the men's favourite piece demanded at all celebrations. A crestfallen band is a sad sight. Sally quickly recovered and forgave. She stood in the doorway in her long wedding-dress with the puffed sleeves, heliotrope, her favourite colour, with touches of Buckinghamshire-lace at her neck and wrists, holding her bouquet, her hair only a little ruffled and smiling more and more with every turn of the jigging air as the bystanders smiled and clapped in rhythm. George drew himself to his full height at her side, possessive and assured in his black jacket and white waistcoat, both buttoned high, his cravat and grey striped trousers, his smile now broad in appreciation of the thought which counted that afternoon.

The polka was repeated by request, for several in the lane had picked up their skirts, being carried quite away, before the men withdrew, bedecked with the remaining confetti and playing a march.

The date had been April the Second. 'A near thing', George said as the strains died away, passing the Cross Tree, 'a very near thing all round'.

Ada and Harry Blindell, settled next door, were congenially matched but opposite in appearance and demeanour. She was tall, elegant and quietly spoken. Harry was outspoken, short in stature and awkward in movement being lame, which was, perhaps, why he was a tailor.

Their kitchen, that with the bread-oven, low-ceilinged but wide enough, was soon half taken over by his treadle sewing-machine, ironing-boards, heavy steam-irons and wide table, which was pushed to the pond-side window and so to the best daylight. He would climb with difficulty to sit there cross-legged for his hand-sewing. His materials were those of the quality, the bettermost classes, as the villagers spoke of them — heavy yet soft serges, thorn-proof cords, tweeds which almost smelt of northern heather, lining-silks of rich sheen, collar-velvets soft as down to the touch. 'A pleasure to put scissors to them, a real pleasure', Harry used to say. Often before the open window he hummed and sang as he chalked, snicked, tacked and fine-stitched. His walrus moustache undulated with excerpts from famous oratorios, for his bass voice had assisted choirs in the Crystal Palace itself. Its tones echoed the Handel organ — 'Heavenly, the choruses', he said, 'and the organ magnificent' and then, after a pause for the careful reversal of a half-made cuff: *Oh ruddier than the cherry and riper than the berry and nymph more bright* — perp, perp, perp! What times they were! Never mind — work to be done, work to be done'.

The shire-horses from the farm lumbered down to their drinking-place at the pond when the day's work was done, or passed to and fro in their work with no interest in tailoring. Passers-by would smile, wave or nod and Harry would flash a thimble.

George Chapman the out-door man, herdsman, rick-builder and gardener, for Fred Lester of the adjoining farm, lived beside the tailor who never allowed anyone to think him country-born for a single moment, rather one whose experiences and professed knowledge of the outside world were wide beyond local comprehension and, sometimes, belief. Because of his propensity to enlarge on these in authoritative tones he earned for himself the appellation *Old Philosophy*. He seemed not to mind.

Side by side there began a joint founding of families 'in a domiciliary adjacency propitious in juxta-position', Harry's words: he liked to astound the natives with a lively phrase.

First Vilona Blindell, brown-eyed, brown-haired, contrived to be a beginner, beating to the light tiny Hubert Chapman by twelve days, a clever move and one he was not permitted to forget through all their earliest years. The first-names had to be such as the village had not met before in first-borns vying from the first glimpse of daylight. At proper intervals, there was a build-up for 'Lona of three sisters and a brother and, next-door, additions of two sisters and three brothers — two young families growing up side by side, playing together, competing at times, falling out and making up again. The elder ones began school together, raced down the village street at home-time together, full speed down the lane — 'they Weir children. Look at 'em, going as if there's not a minute to live'.

They adopted each other's visiting relatives, the Chapmans' Uncle Jess and Aunt Amy Wright, jolly and young, riding to Claydon on shining bicycles from Bucknell Lodge Farm near Bicester, fourteen miles away, and the Blindells' Aunt Sugar from London and Uncle Bob Pretty, also from the

Smoke, a dapper man in knee-breeches and woollen stockings, who brought a camera on a tripod and a black velvet head-cover, to record country life from all angles. He whistled and joked before small Blindell and Chapman sitters incapable of posing and fixedly unmoved in a situation too tense and novel for any pandering to levity. Studying a result from this he frowned and declared that his camera really must try harder, or perhaps the dicky-bird was moulting, off-song. Ada's father came to live with the Blindells in spells and became Grampy Dick Jennings to everyone.

The converted dairy across the Yard, in view from the other cottage doorways, was a home of striking quietness and order where lived Granny and Will Hughes. They had occupied it since first it became a cottage. Forty and more years ago the dairy-maid from Shepton Mallet in Somerset had come to the new Bernwood Farm dairy and there, or somewhere near it, had captivated her William. Her voice never lost the soft curdled tones of the West Country. Thick-set now, in her high-necked blouse and her black apron for mornings and the starched white one for afternoons when her house-work was done, she could look grim from a firmly-set mouth while the light in her eyes belied it. White hair framed a face which must have been handsomely plump when Will succumbed. She was Granny to all in the Yard. Will, though, was self-effacing, quiet and not even a teaser, as countrymen could be with children all around them. He did light work on the farm and out-did all comers in the growing of flowers and vegetables. His brown eyes shone when he was pleased, but his words were few — he seemed content to be going gently down-hill after a life-time of hard work.

The young mothers turned to Granny for advice and help should the small children 'turn sadly'. She and Will had reared three girls and four boys of their own, all grown up, some with families living away, so Granny had many different remedies — the mustard-plaster, the hot bread-poultice, the goose-fat on brown-paper applied to a wheezy chest, or camphor in a small porous bag like a neck-lace — 'because the boy's bronical. Hark to his breathing'. More acceptable was the syrupy juice from a large raw onion, sliced, with brown sugar laid between the slices in a basin, this to 'cut the phlegm' after colds and coughs. The steaming kettle was installed if real bronchitis threatened. Ipecacuanha was the recommended emetic and Parish's Chemical Food to build you up and nasty pink, grating stuff it was, but good for you because of the iron it contained. Sally and Ada went first to Granny, called Doctor Vaisey from Winslow only if she advised it. What she proposed was followed and had to be endured, the line of her mouth enjoined and achieved it — 'good for you. Come on, child — take it down, all of it. I shall want the spoon back. There — I told you it was a nice taste!'

In return the children when recovered ranged over the Bernwood fields in spring and summer for cowslips first and then for dandelion flower-heads for her wine-making. That she was also an eager maker of black-puddings when a village pig came to his end was something they cared not to think about. Her ebony links and loops were praised and sought after by adults about the village, but the children drew back however invitingly they sizzled next to the bacon-rashers in the pan. Ever inquisitive, they had observed the preparations from the beginning, especially the cleaning of the skins in many scalding waters. 'You're not obliged to look', Granny would say, 'Go and see what help you can give your mothers'. She had authority based on the health and vigour of her own family. It could be seen when they visited. They claimed with smiles that they still belonged, that their thoughts never strayed far from the Yard. Their children absolutely asserted their rights in it, although grandson Rowland, on holiday from some far city school, was challenged on the basis of flaming red hair and preposterous freckles seen nowhere else in any of the Hughes families. In blazer and cap he adopted superior airs regarding 'your silly old country games', played in the triangle of cobbles and grass which was the communal Yard. He was written off, the only one, as not worth waiting for and was very different from Alice, the eldest grand-child of all. She was surely a replica of the dairy-maid of long ago. Slim, but the same height as Granny, she had brown hair framing her face just as Granny's. For her leadership and readiness for adventures she was one most impatiently awaited. Will smiled continuously when she was around: 'Jane all over again', he said, 'the very same' and he gently stroked his side-whiskers. The similarity was to be seen in her tall mother, but best of all in Alice, something to do with 'jumping a generation' the adults said, but this baffled young listeners. Well, yes — Alice was a jolly good jumper and climber too — and skipper.

Her mother, Clara, was joint-caretaker with her husband of the village-hall, library and games-rooms. He was an ex-army drill-instructor and a dazzling swordsman, who ran gymnastic classes for young men of the village, and sometimes he drew Alice into his performances at displays, socials and the occasional grand Liberal Demonstration on the Claydon House lawn.

One such display in the village-hall was watched in trepidation, because it involved a long, straight sword. Children leaned back and gripped their chair-seats, or their parents' arms, while their parents affected calmness, though admitting qualms — 'case anything goes wrong'. There stood Alice sideways on towards the front of the stage, her head bent forward so that an apple could be placed on the smooth and pretty nape of her neck. Sideways, too, she smiled her beguiling smile her hands clasped before her, while her father, tall and muscular in singlet and long white trousers, flexed his arms and checked his grasp on the hilt of the sword, which flashed along its length as he stepped to the front of the stage.

'If you please', he said, 'I must have your help in this performance. I can cut the apple in halves with one stroke of my sword only in complete silence' and here he carefully felt its edge with his thumb, 'so, please, not a sound and not a movement'. As he moved to position himself behind Alice a deathly hush and awed stillness fell upon his audience. He began with preliminary wide sweeps in the air, then raised the sword high and straight to bring it carefully and slowly down, lightly touching the apple. Then he raised it again to full height to bring it down in a single swift flash and the apple fell in two clean pieces to the stage. To a deep general gasp and worried cheers Sergeant Frank Daniels and daughter Alice stepped hand-in-hand to the front smiling and bowing. There was never the remotest question of Alice's rights in the Yard.

Granny and Will provided sensation one morning when Fred, their soldier son, strode to their door, home on leave after years of absence, a man only imagined by the children until that moment. He had been it was said on the North-West Frontier of India; the most dangerous place in the world, where fierce, wily natives — in those days no-one hesitated to call them such — continually menaced the British troops stationed there. Only fearsome Lancers such as he could hold them back. However, he failed to bring his lance with him. Otherwise, he was magnificent in his walking-out uniform, tunic grandly braided and shinily buttoned right to the chin, beautiful wide red stripes down the outsides of his trouser-legs, his toe-caps a dazzle to the eyes, clipped moustache, deep tan and eyes startlingly alert. No child of the Yard dared to speak to him.

Almost at once he won for himself a wife from North Marston, the village beyond the valley, and so, when his term of service was done, he provided for Sally of the Yard a friend in another Alice, in nature not unlike young Alice of the sliced apple.

The Yard children were awake, up and about at first light on the day of the other wedding which was so strangely an affair of laughter, bright talk and tears, very many more of these than are usual. It was the wedding of Kate, the youngest and the only unmarried daughter of Granny and Will, and a last son-in-law. The ceremony done there was then a great gathering in the Yard, neighbours and friends and all the Hughes families who out-numbered them all. It was such a warm and sunny summer day that trestle-tables could be set up on the grass for an open-air reception, for great bustlings to and fro and speeches and Kate laughing and crying, hugging first Granny and then Will and then both together and finally a moving off with trunks and wrappings, flowers and confetti which left the children standing silent and quite bewildered. Kate and her husband were going to Canada to live in a strange place far away, a place surely nothing like so friendly and homely as the Weir, Botolph Claydon, in England.

A great company watched them begin their journey in a be-decked fly, the driver with a button-hole and a bow of white ribbon on his whip, the excited cob with a rosette and sprinklings of confetti, thrown now with little heart. They trotted the adventurers away, they leaning and waving from the windows, along the lane beside the Weir water to disappear with them into a heavy blankness beyond the Cross Tree. For a long moment no one moved. Poor Granny stood bowed and overwhelmed, as Will, with his arm round her, whispered: 'There — there, Jane-y', looking helplessly at a loss.

It left young Hubert of the Chapmans fearfully anxious for the travellers, alarmed, because Sally, his mother, had told him that when she was a small girl her father, Grampy Amos Wright, *nearly* emigrated to Winnipeg, right in the middle of Canada. It was as she explained it, because of the hard times of the 1880's, but, after all, in the end he did not go. Mercifully, he became a farm-bailiff instead. Relief about this was intense. The thought that a small Claydon boy could so easily become a Canadian of some sort alarmed him. Worse, he might get himself abducted by a tribe of Red Indians and be turned into a Huron, or an Algonquin, with eagle's feathers in his hair and paintings on his chest. If not this, then at least he might be a small Pale Face amongst brown and red-skinned strangers. And, besides, how could anyone satisfactorily settle in a place so ridiculously named? And now two people were riding off to Saskatchewan, a name to defy imagination.

The Yard was quiet for a long time because of this. Granny and Will were tight-lipped, for Kate was their darling, their youngest and letters took weeks, sometimes months, to come and go. Then one morning a photograph arrived, which all in the Yard crowded to see, of the new Canadians standing arm-in-arm in the wide porch of a neat wooden house, smiling happily. Hubert, pushing to see, had to admit to himself that they appeared to be contented. He wondered then whether around the year 1885, in the remote past, he had missed something important, the opportunity to become a Mountie, perhaps, in a broad-brimmed hat, pointed in the crown, a scarlet tunic and those wide riding-breeches and shining leggings, mounted on a mettlesome horse, groomed to perfection; or, perhaps, to be a farmer in the Golden West, that boundless ocean of rippling corn, with never a tree in sight and granaries reaching to the sky. There was adult talk of the acres of prairie land the Canadian Government would actually give you for a start — you only had to fence it, build yourself a cabin and begin. What if you, infinitesimally small, had settled in Winnipeg in 1885?

However, for the time being, there was comfort in having a known home-place and known people around and some certainties against unexpected contingencies such as the wedding celebration in the Yard and that fraught departure along the lane. As with most children everyday concerns soon displace such things, so it was with the Yard children, although Lona did say that she wouldn't mind living in a nice wooden house like that one in Canada, whilst declining absolutely the smallest possible adventure nearer home. This was to climb along the fence of wooden posts and strung wire, standing inwards from the edge of the pond to mark off a drinking-place for cattle, there to sit on a post to watch the wavelets on the water and enjoy a great surprise. As he would not reveal what this was to be, clever-stick Hubert could do it himself if he wished. It was about the silliest idea Lona had ever heard of and she left to find her sister Nora and Eva of next-door who were already playing 'Houses' somewhere.

When told of this, school-mate Harry Wiggins said with scorn, 'Well — 'course she wouldn't! Girls — no good for anything.' At ten years this Harry also had strong opinions. He shared the discovery that by climbing along to his personal post next to his friend, to look down with him at the moving water, they could feel themselves travelling far and wide on smooth voyages at will. They had realised this suddenly when fishing for stickle-backs on a sunny morning when a strong wind was whipping the water into sheets of fleeting ripples. The amazing discovery was unsteadying at first, the starting-off being sudden. Coming home again was simple. You raised your gaze and lo, you were in port. A good breeze, a sunny day and calm concentration were the only requirements. Harry was right — no girl could be expected to appreciate the wonder of it, so they kept the pleasure of it to themselves for a time, Hubert could see in imagination what Winnipeg was really like, also Saskatchewan, and Harry could set off round the globe for New Zealand, because that was said to be about as far as anyone could sail in this world.

Yard people, Claydon people, large and small were quite capable of looking beyond the confines of the Weir and the village while staying as comfortably as could be at home.

THE WEIR POND

The Weir children regularly spoke of the pond as theirs. The posts and wire marking off the drinking-places for cattle, those where the boys sat to day-dream and the others at the field end, were seen as the limits of the farm, put there by the squire of the previous generation, a man past-master in the preservation of boundaries. All the rest of the water lying directly before the cottages, then turning away as if to reach the Cross Tree, was regarded by the village as belonging to the Weir people. Fred Lester & Sons of the farm used it, just as the Weir children ranged over their fields, played hide-and-seek in their rick-yard, climbed about their empty hay-wagons, ventured upstairs into the granary to see if straying hens had laid eggs there, or to watch the noisy grinding of cattle-cake, or just to feel the oiliness of the stacked fleeces after the June shearing.

In the passing seasons the children would say: 'There's a kingfisher just come to our pond — come and see', or: 'We've got stickle-backs that sing in our pond', to invite the scornful response, *'Liar'*, or, in heavy rains: 'Our pond's half over the lane — Harry Blindell rode into it on his trike in the dark', or, in time of frost: 'Our pond's froze over. Coming down for slides?', or, in summer drought: 'You can walk all over our pond. It's all dried up. Come and see — there's dead mud-fish.'

School friends came by invitation: others were warily inspected, except on the occasional grand celebrations on the ice when skaters and sliders made it a gathering-place for most of the village for many hours, joyfully, tirelessly in a whirl wondrously provided. Boys enlisted the farm men to cut slides of prodigious length, while older children ventured to the frightening place under the over-hanging trees, where the ice was smooth as glass and the pond's depth beneath it inky and awesome. 'Reckon our pond's deeper than people say. Come away', they would say and then try to forget it by sliding furiously along the new slide's full length.

On consideration Hubert and Harry decided that Sid Jennings, from down-the-village, could be invited to share their pleasure in effortless travel, so one spring morning they got him to sit on a third post next to them above the moving water, to be specially privileged, because he was, on the whole, a good sport, ever ready to try anything new. At ten years all three were prepared to entertain anything, as they would say, 'different'.

'Well — tell me what to do. Sitting here's not much,' he said, settling with difficulty and gazing around.

'Keep still and sit tight. That's all you've got to do, Sid,' Hubert explained, 'except you've got to keep looking down at the waves like Harry and me. Then you'll go.'

Gripping his post, his feet unsteady in the wire, Sid stared at the wavelets which the breeze pushed urgently, sparklingly along, as Harry and Hubert, almost at once, and together, cried: 'Going — going, Sid. We're off. Started yet?'

'Started? Started where? Can't see anything — I'm still here on this post.'

'You don't have to *see* anything, Sid, except the waves. Fix your eyes on 'em hard — keep looking down — then you'll go — sudden.'

'I *am* looking down. All I can see is the water bringing that egg-shell along and I'm going to get it.'

Edging to the bank he waited for it, captured it, whereupon the travellers raised their eyes and returned to harbour, shouting: 'Dafty! You didn't give it a chance. Come back and have another go.'

Sid examined the shell and then looked across in clear, cold disbelief and deep scorn: 'Not me,' he said, 'and dafty yourselves. You're making it all up to have me on. You're not catching me. Try it on somebody else. Here — catch this, it's only a starling's' and off he went back along the lane without turning his head.

'Let him go, Hubert,' Harry said. 'Where did you sail to this time?'

'Pacific Ocean — farther than Canada.'

They sat for a while deciding that Sid was a born land-lubber. It had been foolish to waste time on him. So they watched, as the breeze started new eddies on the surface of the water, how they spread, raced and faded at the shore, how, if you watched the shore, the trees, the lane, anything but the moving water, you stayed, like Sid, immovably in Botolph

Claydon, England. After a while Harry said, 'Lucky you —
living at the Wire, the pond and farm and all — better'n down
where I live and Sid.'

'Not the Wire, really,' Hubert said.

'My dad,' went on Harry, 'says it's because of this wire
and the other at the far end that keeps the animals back, else
some would swim through and get away.'

'Well, you're dad's wrong then. My dad says it's Weir,
like on the letters and it's because of the bank.'

'Bank?'

'Yes — the bank, look, that stops the water from
running away down the fields. He says some old farmer called
Bone, hundreds of years ago, built it up to make the pond
because it's got good springs in it. So it's been a sort of weir
ever since, Bone's Weir!'

'Oh,' Harry said. 'Well — only sort of,' gazing across
at the grassy mound, raised long ago and, that morning, adorned
by butter-cups and moon-daisies.

'Yes, only sort of, Harry. Come on — what about it?
Let's do something different.'

Spring was bursting out all around them, birds singing
deliriously right at hand, may blossom tossing in the hedge,
sunlight dancing on the water and it was Saturday morning,
school a million miles away — action, action must follow.

'I know,' Harry said, 'Move off. See if the moor-hen's
laid again. You had yesterday's — mine today.' They moved off
and then skirted the water margin to reach the spot where reeds
and half-drowned fallen tree-branches made a haven for the
timorous, scuttling creatures. Approaching with ease and
making no sound, they peered over to the thickest cluster of
reeds, well away from their reach, where, artfully placed, was
the nest. She was not at home.

'Look, Harry — four eggs. She's laid again. Stay here
and get the clay while I fetch a bean-stick.'

That was quickly done, also the moulding of Harry's
wet clay to the end of the stick.

'Your egg, Harry — you dip,' so with trembling care,
his boots sinking slowly into the soft verge and holding his
breath, Harry put the clay to the dainty clutch in the nest. An
egg stuck. Carefully, steadily, still not breathing, he withdrew to

place the frail, speckled creation in the hollow of his hand.

'Warm, Hubert — feel. Mustn't take another or she'll forsake.'

'Course, Harry. What'll you do with it?'

'Blow it. This is the first moor-hen's I've got.'

'Come on, then. My mum will look after it till you go home.'

Looking back as they left the reedy spot they saw the mother moor-hen's head bobbing in the farthest reeds. She was creeping back to the nest.

The boys saw nothing wrong in this — conservation had not yet become a concern. True, each spring the local policeman put a printed paper on the parish notice-board, all in small black lettering, which listed the wild birds whose nests it was forbidden to rob, stressing penalty. No-one took the slightest notice of it. Boys vied in making collections taken personally, swops not counting. If in the density of a tall hedge of fierce thorn one secured a tiny egg from the ball-like nest of the little bum-barrels it was a triumph occasioning no qualm, but for the thorns. The police-sergeant's list spoke only of long-tailed tits — bum-barrels were not mentioned.

The boys nestled Harry's egg in cotton-wool in one of Sally's kitchen saucers and then ambled to the Cross Tree seat, where was no sign of Sid, or of anyone else, so they sat idly for a while until, quite near, came the sound of Sid's voice: 'I've got the pole, Eddy. Is it heavy? — You're wobbling with it. I bet it's heavy, Ed.' They rose and swiftly ran to the rear of George Norman's cottage which stood near-by. From the jumble of old hay and straw, calf-shed, broken ladder and wood-pile a grunting figure was emerging bearing a large wooden wash-tub, best borne inverted over the head. Because there was no forward view the foot-steps were hesitant and progress slow and, holding a long wooden pole, was Sid, watching anxiously. Mystified, Hubert and Harry climbed the rickety gate.

'Course it's heavy,' boomed Eddy from within the tub. 'Get in front of me now, Sid, and I'll follow.'

'What's on?' yelled Harry.

'What's on, Sid?' echoed Hubert — 'this looks daft, if you like.'

'Wait and see,' Sid answered. 'Open the gate for us —

wide and keep out of our way.'

Slowly the procession advanced, Sid awkwardly managing the pole, Eddy groping at his heels, all, presumably, that he could see. They opened the gate exclaiming, 'Coo — this is something, Sid. We're coming with you.'

'Keep right out of our way, then,' Sid said,' or I might crack you with this pole — it swings.'

Arrived at the gateway he turned into the lane and then made for the pond, Eddy now pacing carefully behind him, next breaking into hollow echoing song. *Across the ocean wide we sail in sunshine, rain and snow and hail — Ship ahoy* ! Who's with you, Sid? Keep on level ground — don't let me trip.'

'Keep going, Ed,' Sid said, 'we're nearly there.'

'Sailing — that's what it is, Harry. Keep with 'em,' Hubert urged, both trotting alongside, 'this 'ull be good.'

When they reached the Weir's verge Eddy heaved the tub from his shoulders and lowered it to his feet and Sid laid down the pole. Eddy puffed, easing his neck and working his cramped arms. Then, because Hubert and Harry stood gazing solemnly at the tub, he said, 'Not wanted now — found it in the back of the shed.'

Eddy's mother had been the user of it, taking in mountains of other people's laundry. She had been a good washer and ironer, in demand even beyond the village and a mainstay in her home. For a year now her great wash tub had not been needed. The boys stood perplexed and worried, feeling again the sadness over which the adults still shook their heads, though understanding little why. 'Worn out,' people continued to say, 'now she's got the rest she never had time for many a year, poor woman.' George Norman was a widower whose other sons were grown men who had left home, one by one, for independence. He and fifteen-year old Eddy lived in permanent disarray.

'Does your dad know?' Hubert asked.

'That he don't, I made sure of that. He's down in the bottom field singling swedes. Come on — help me get it on the water.' The boys at that threw off their momentary thoughts and put their hands to the heavy tub — adventure, imminent excitement, lay right at their feet.

'Heave and push,' Eddy commanded, Harry eagerly saying, 'Can we have turns sailing, Eddy?'

'Not till I've been across and back again and Sid has first go.'

'Yes, don't forget that, you two,' put in Sid, for here was real sailing not make-up stuff while sitting on posts. All now pushed until the tub was on the water when, taking the pole from Sid, Eddy stepped in, feet wide apart — 'else I'll wobble', he said. He put the pole to the bank, pushed hard and gradually got himself fully afloat — 'Going — moving, look!' he said and now he could use the pole, punting style, gingerly taking the open water.

'Good old Ed,' Sid shouted in glee, 'my first go, then you two after.' 'Yes, you first,' the two agreed. Poling was difficult for the Weir's muddy bottom gripped the pole and the tub strongly wished to rotate. However, soon Eddy contrived a rough-and-ready forward movement and the bank receded as slowly he made for the wide water where the pond turned away for Bone's bank, smooth, inviting water. 'Golly Eddy — I'm for that!', Harry shouted leaping, jigging almost into the water.

'My first go,' Sid said, 'don't forget how I helped. Going right round to the far end, are you, Eddy?'

'Course I am,' he called, poling now with a little style, smiling broadly and approaching the farthest point from any shore.

At that moment swiftly deciding and saying, 'I'm going to fetch the others,' Hubert left, running fast.

'What's wrong?' Harry called.

'Going to fetch Lona and the others to see. You fetch your Florrie. Sid, you fetch Gwen.'

'Not me — I'm staying here,' Sid called back.

'Me too,' Harry also called, firmly unmoved, and then, across the water, 'Hi, Eddy! Why have you stopped, Eddy?'

In that widest stretch of water Eddy was stationary. His pole upright and apparently immovable, he was clinging to it as the tub turned slowly round it as if determined to return to base. In sudden concern he cried, 'The pole's stuck and water's coming in. I'm standing in water. It's coming through the sides. I can't move.'

Racing, skipping and laughing came Lona, Hubert and a gathering of other children, hurrying to the scene, not sensing Eddy's difficulty and eager to cheer his crossing and welcome his triumphant return. Suddenly they halted and stood in fright, for Eddy, now extremely alarmed was shouting, 'More is coming in — it's coming in fast. I've got to get to the bank.' He gave a frantic wrench to the pole which came free only to give him and the tub a heavy lurch so that water over-topped the vessel's brim, and came pouring in. Eddy and the wash-tub together began gradually to sink.

'Can't somebody do something?' he shouted, 'the tub's going to the bottom!'

'What? How?' the watchers cried, crowding to the margin, dreadfully sobered. 'You'll have to get out and swim, or walk,' something Eddy knew he must do at once. As he put a leg over the side the tub gave a great gurgle and sank from sight and Eddy, neither in nor out, sank with it. When at last he ceased to sink he stood with Weir water reaching his arm-pits, deathly pale but with a look of immense relief on his face, the pole still in his grasp.

Already Hubert had found his father who came hurrying with a long-handled garden hoe in hand, saying, 'Don't worry — Eddy won't drown — get a trifle damp, that's all. Bring the pole if you can, Eddy, then we can give you a pull.'

Very slowly, the pole raised above the water, Eddy pushed his way to the side, George extending the hoe for his grasp helped with a final heave to the bank, where Eddy finally stood drenched to his chin, his feet oozing lumps of black mud. Then everyone laughed, Eddy too, though gasping for breath and tottering almost into the water again. And everyone laughed once more when George said, 'Now we know how deep the old pond is, Eddy has measured it for us — but don't stand there a minute longer, boy, or you'll catch your death after all. Get home fast and into some dry clothes before your dad comes home to his dinner.'

That thought sent Eddy off at a grotesque gallop, leaving behind him a trail of pond-water, paddlings of mud and duck-weed right to his father's yard-gate and then in.

'I never had my ride,' Sid moaned, but everyone else

fell silent as they gazed far over the water at the spot where Eddy and the wash-tub had sunk.

Harry said, 'He'll never get the tub back — full of water and fixed in the mud,' while Lona said, 'Boys! — too clever by half, you can see that' and George, leaning on his hoe and gently smiling, said, 'Yes, Lona, that tub must have been bone-dry. Its slats had shrunk. It was bound to let water in. If Eddy had had it soaking for a couple of days he could have been half-way to France by this time.'

All stood looking again over the water and then George said, 'Dinner-time now for everybody, I'll warrant, and, for once, I've got master Hubert right on time.'

'Me and Harry call for you after dinner, Hubert?' Sid called.

'Your egg, Harry — have it later on,' Hubert called in turn. As they went Lona said, 'I say, would you really have gone all by yourself in that old tub?' Carefully choosing his words Hubert replied, 'I might — you never know. Anyhow, would you? Answer me that.' Again he turned to look at the fatal spot where lay a vessel betrayed and lost, the water's surface innocent, undisturbed, hardly a ripple showing. It had been a thoroughly satisfactory spring morning. No boy could have hoped for more.

In the afternoon there was scooping up frog-spawn. Sid and Harry brought one or two outsiders for this, permission given. When they departed with their jam-jars of promise, the trio got to work on a big project, the construction in the pond-side mud of a system of canals, miniature docks, harbours, bridges and jetties at the field end where they had a view down the vista of water of over-hanging elms, wayward hedge-sides and reeds and of Hubert's home with its distinctive pattern of wall-timbers and thatch, the front room window, Sally's lace-curtains and geraniums — everything upside down in the broken water.

Nor had it been an idle boast about the Weir's singing stickle-backs. Harry and Sid bore witness when, the harbour-work done, several, for proof, were captured and placed in a tin of pond-water, with weed and friendly stones for them to swim around. In turn, ears close to the water, they declared they discerned the faint high-pitched, squeaky continuous sounds, or they declared they heard them to please Hubert. Sid said it was the fishes' spines touching the sides of the tin as the restless creatures darted, turned, twisted and apparently squabbled in incessant efforts to find wide water again. 'Put 'em back in the pond,' Harry advised. 'Sid and me — we'll say we heard 'em too and let the school-kids call *us* liars, eh, Sid?'

'Yes,' answered Sid, dangerously, 'let 'em try.'

All this took them to their separate tea-times. Harry nursing his egg was ending a day around the pond fruitful through every minute, with the special pleasure, later, of informing anyone who did not know already that there had almost been a fatality at the Weir in the morning, certainly a vessel lost, and its navigator confined to his bed. George Norman, in a fearful taking, had locked away all Eddy's clean dry clothes until further notice.

This was well savoured by the gossips and pipe-smokers at the Cross Tree seat. Eddy was released the next morning for a full day of swede-singling beside his father in the bottom field and when at the end of the day he ventured to join the company at the tree he was quickly made aware that his famous voyage would go down in village history. 'Hold your head high, Captain,' said one, 'you went down with your ship!'

The pond settled again into its day-to-day busyness, the days lengthening and summer steadily advancing.

If the king-fisher, the coots, dab-chicks and old Moll Hern, the heron, standing on one leg at the field end for all of ten minutes, were only occasional visitors, moor-hens, voles, frogs, efts, stickle-backs, minnows and mud-fish were regulars.

Since, with the bringing of piped water to the farm some years later, the pond fell into disuse to be over-grown by bulrushes and then to become a weedy marsh, it is probable that some inhabit it still. In the halcyon days a fleet of Miss Hilda Lester's Aylesbury ducks patterned the pond's surface in a kind of calm ownership. She was the teenage daughter who enticed them home every evening by calling: 'Dilly-dilly-dilly', while rattling the corn in their food-bowl and the iron latch of their night-shelter. They hurried to shore and then waddled to her in procession, quacking in chorus, furiously wagging their bottoms from side to side, avid to shovel up their suppers thrown into the shelter, which she then smartly closed on them for the night. It was a summer ritual that comfortably ended another day and was a sign to the yard children still at play that it was their bed-time too, when Sally often called likewise: 'Dilly-dilly time to come in,' and Ada Blindell shoo-ed her last reluctant small one in.

The martins returned and were now quite frantically taking pond-mud to complete their nests. These, in a row under the eaves of the granary which oversaw the Blindell's cottage, were skilful renovations of the dry, cup-like nests sheltered there year after year. Fierce squabbling on the martins' arrival meant that lazy nesting house-sparrows had first to be ejected in scenes of all-round indignation.

Harry Blindell, sitting at his sewing-machine in the window-alcove below the new-comers, could see all their new work and could, if he wished, measure the pace of their building against his own french-seaming, running and felling.

In a morning of furious business beneath the eaves, while watching him at work, Hubert once said, 'Mr Blindell — the nests look all the same. How do the birds know which are their proper homes?'

Harry paused from his treadling to look up at the twittering creatures' fresh layers of mud, then answered, 'Say you've fallen down and hurt your poor knee. Do you make any mistake about where to run to get it kissed better? And when you run home from school, all out of breath and wanting your dinner, you don't run to our door, do you? — any more than Lona, Alice and Norry run to yours.'

'No,' Hubert agreed, 'I expect they just know the same as we do.' Resuming his work and displaying the neat exact turning of a cuff, Harry then said, 'You like watching me at my machine. Thinking of being a tailor one day?'

'No!' answered Hubert at once, quite alarmed, 'no, not really. I think I'd better go now and see what the others are doing.' As he ran to join a yard game he heard the machine start up again, sweetly whirring and then Harry Blindell's loud laughter and next his deep voice reverberating *'No wonder beauty's queen with him would not be seen —'* Hubert knew for certain that tailoring was not for him and from that same moment.

In the front room of a quiet summer evening after tea,

George was reading the Buckingham Advertiser, Sally turning the heel of a black school stocking while the children were at the table building houses with picture-postcards, when George, smiling gently, lowered his paper to say, 'We never lack visitors.' Sally cried out, dropping her knitting, 'Where? Where is he? Get him — you know I can't abide them.' A pond-newt, an eft, was out exploring and having crossed the lane to climb the grass-bank before the house-door, had penetrated the outer passage, finally to fall helplessly down the deep step into the room for a bewildered look round. Cardboard house at once abandoned, the children sped to capture him, to hold him, cold, squashy and wriggling as George rose, with Sally urging, 'Do something with him, Dad. Take him where he belongs — you know how they give me the shivers. Hold him gently, though, you children. I can't think why such creatures were ever created!'

'Just what he's thinking about us,' George said, taking him in hand and bringing him close. 'Look — there's the very thought in his bright little eyes.'

'Rubbish!' she said — 'all the same, since he's made, he has as much right as the rest of us to take a look round. I only wish they would look somewhere else. Get him to the pond, do,' and George, the children closely with him, returned him gently to the water, where he struck out like a champion swimmer and was away in a second. Returning George said, 'I think that one is getting to know us — only wants to be neighbourly.'

'In that case,' Sally said in a final riposte, 'everybody must close the front-door behind them. Who left it open this time?' The newts were easily the quietest of all the yard's neighbours, never uttering a sound, were merely inquisitive and happiest of all when wet again.

As to sound, apart from the ducks' friendly quacking and the crk-crk-crk of the moor-hens, the pond also attracted the maddening evening *'Come-back, come-back, come-back'* of Lesters' guinea-fowl, a restless family, perpetually in protest, who chose the high elms above the pond for their roosts. They made such a noisy fluttering, screeching business of it as the sun went down, chorusing continuously as they scrambled to the highest branches, that Sally would stand laughing in the fading light, calling: 'Get to bed, do. Come-back? Where from?'

George said, 'They worry lest a wandering fox has spied them. High in the trees and the pond-water below them they are safe enough, however much they worry.'

'They spend their lives worrying,' Sally said, 'and practising just one tune, but, there, with the silly little bobbing heads they've got, I expect they know no better.'

Other noisy neighbours were the screech-owls. The children disliked their sudden single cries, sometimes far-off, sometimes too near, especially on dark nights when the wind roared in the chimney-breast and shook the leaded panes behind the window-curtains.

'They sound as if they would dive at you,' Hubert said once, to which Sally replied, extending only a very little comfort: 'They'd take one look at you and then fly to the farthest tree.' Outside in the dark, well away on the far side of the curtains and the window was the best place for them. They and the guinea-fowl were intruders and were accorded no rights in the pond. They sat high above the water having no friends.

The martins were different. Their mud-gathering done they skimmed the water for food. When their young were hatched they criss-crossed from dawn until dark, twittering continuously, never colliding, delivering their catch to their front-door under the eaves to a clamour of gaping beaks, yellow as egg-yolk.

When an outing was arranged, or proposed, the yard children pressed to the windows to watch the water. The pond would inform them — rain-spots, or just flies, a big spot and sudden alarm — no, a dragon-fly and relief. For a prestigious visit to Aunt Sugar in far-away London the Blindells must first walk to Granborough Road Station. Fine weather was essential — 'Sunday-Best clothes for the Metropolis,' declared Harry, 'pray for the heavens to be kind;' so Lona and Alice, the chosen travellers, who would travel in charge of the guard, wished and watched, their hair-curlers in till the very last moment.

For the fourteen-mile drive to Bucknell Lodge Farm on the far side of Bicester the Chapman children were wide awake at first light. The double-hooded four-wheeler, hired for the day from Johnny Webb at the village shop, was exciting in itself, George would drive the whole family. There would be Sunday dinner with Grampy Amos and Granny Hannah Wright and four jolly aunts and uncles, an afternoon of fun and certain spoiling, an uproarious tea-time and then the ride home in the dark. So, all young faces at the front window, the pond was watched as never before — yes, if flies only were dimpling its calmness the expedition would be on.

Big spots and bigger spots and more of them dotting the surface, definitely rain, and soon more rain and then sheets of rain, would settle the matter completely. There came then a day of endless fretting and an early bed-time to see, as Sally said, what another day would bring for she had had 'enough of children this day, so to bed with you'. Her tucking-in was quite fierce as she said she wanted to hear not a single word till morning. Then George, after an interval, would call from the foot of the stairs, 'Are you children asleep?' to which there would be either no reply, or just a careful, yawning, drowsy-sounding, 'Ye-e-s.' With patience a fine Sunday might dawn as the pond reported favourably and then the expedition would be on. Patience, Sally regularly asserted, somewhat enigmatically, was good for the gout.

During summer tea-times in the front-room with the whole family at the table, the pond sometimes produced a wonder ever fascinating to the children and often an astonishment to visitors. It was special to that room, nowhere else. In high summer the westering sun cast its rays on the water at exactly the angle to reflect them directly through the window for a wavering pattern of light to dance high in the far corner of the room, never still, never for a second the same. It was a puzzle and a delight to young eyes and Sally would say, 'Pull the curtains right back. Let the blessed sunshine in — all of it that wants to come' and George, 'We know we've got summer truly with us now — the old pond is showing us once again in its quiet way.' Hubert nourished a small smug satisfaction in it. Who else in all Claydon, even in the yard, or at the farm, had such a marvel bestowed on them?

With hay-making begun there came once a memorable season when no rain fell for week after week, when the sky was cloudless from sun-rise to sunset, when at night moon and stars were set in a faultless dome, when the clayey surfaces of the fields baked hard and opened with deep cracks.

First the smaller ponds dried up and then for the first time in living memory the Weir water shrank away. The posts where Harry and Hubert had sat for their dream-travelling stood in a sea of glistening mud, which, in a few days, dried to resemble the skin of an old elephant, littered by all kinds of revelations — bricks, great stones, tins, mysterious iron-work, tree-wood and, far over where Eddy Norman gave up water-travel, a black hulk fixed in the mud, Eddy's wash-tub.

So, when the children had said, 'Our pond's all dried up' it was truth and when a few days later they claimed, 'You can walk right across to the field — come and see and try it,' they set about proving it, with special attention given to the derelict, until by weight of numbers, the mud crust began to cave in when they retreated to the lane to gaze on the sad grey expanse and to wonder where the moor-hens had gone, the frogs, the newts and the minnows, stickle-backs and mud-fish. One of these, having gasped its last, lay flat and exposed as if waiting to be cooked. 'Who'd want to eat that?' they said, shuddering.

One sign of life was seen at the field end, where, in the last remaining soft mud, was Lesters' huge matron of a sow happily immersed, her snout, eyes and ears alone visible above the black, oozy mess. Within a few days that paradisal pleasure was denied her, so then she lay on the dried surface in the deepest shade she could find dreaming of what had been.

The villagers called it a 'sad drouth' and Fred Lester and the other farmers a misery everybody could do without. The daily recourse to Claydon Park lakes to fill churns of water and to get this to their cattle complicated their already urgent hay-work. The blazing sun turned the mown grass into hay in a single day and the vital winter fodder had to be rushed to the stacks. If left it lay 'burnt to nothing' in a few hours. Furthermore, the sun and ground-heat brought on the oats, barley and wheat so fast that Lester must reap his oats while the hay was not yet in, or they would shed their precious grain and stand valueless. The farm-men worked over-time, or 'long-time', day after day and neither they nor Lester and his sons, all nut brown and several a little haggard, left work till past sun-down, while daily there was the water to be got for the complaining cattle and then the watering of them.

William Cubbage, native of Middle Claydon, the renowned dowser, was in demand countrywide for the discovery of underground water and when at last Lester got him to Bernwood with his hazel-wand he attracted a gathering of village people and children, including all of the yard, anxious to see what his forked stick would do. William himself was confident, 'On the top of this hill — no place better for a search,' he said and he began testing at once in the farm-paddock, walking steadily about, holding his wand before him by its two prongs until it quivered and then rose strongly as he turned towards the farm-house.

'Steady on William,' Lester interrupted, following closely, 'no help to us this way. Try near the pond if you don't mind.'

'Mind?' William responded sharply, 'who am I to mind? It's the water says where I shall go. It's powerful strong here and I must follow it.' His wand stood more and more vibrant, his grip on it strangely resisted with his every step and his face tense. He turned now directly for the house.

'Hold on William, this won't do. Hold up, man. Digging here's the last thing we want' and Lester, red in the face from annoyance, stood in his way.

'All right, Lester,' William said, actually wrestling with the hazel, 'I'm not saying dig here. What would be the sense? Just let me follow this water out of interest if you don't mind. I shall find where you can dig comfortable enough, but first I've got to find what this water under our feet is saying to me. It's mighty powerful — it's pulling me on.'

'All right, then,' said Lester, now laughing, 'carry on' and William carried on right into the courtyard straight to the farm-kitchen door, where Mrs Lester and other house-people stood aside in sudden alarm.

'Nothing to scare anybody, ma'am. Just let me follow it. I've never felt such a pull as we've got here,' and she and the others made way for him, the usually unsmiling lady saying amusedly, 'Step right in, sir, but you might very well spoil your welcome!' William stepped in to declare that the strongest spring he had ever found in Claydon lay under her dining-room floor.

'Dig there, missis,' he said, 'and you won't want for water no matter how long this drought lasts, and now folks, I'd better see if there's something handier nigh the pond. You try holding my bit of hazel, ma'am — it's cut straight from the hedge,' but, no, she said she dare not touch it and when Lester and his sons took it they felt nothing at all.

'It's not many have the gift,' William said, 'and God knows why it's landed with me. It's taking it out of me proper this summer. See now if I can prove meself down at the pond. It's a wonderful find under your floor; but don't worry, missis, it's well down. You won't drop in.'

At the edge of the pond, close to where the boys had sat for their dreaming, William's rod rose again. 'Strong enough here for you, boss,' he said, 'but you'll have to dig down for it,' and he stood aside for Tom Giles, the carter, and Billy, his son, to strike spades into the dried mud and then deeper until they reached the ancient earth below.

'Deeper — you've got to go deeper,' William ordered, 'the water's there right under your feet, waiting for you,' and then when the diggers were chest-deep in their hole it came in, so suddenly that Tom and Billy had to be nimble to escape it. It welled up, sweet and pure, to a depth of about three feet and then stopped.

'There you are, Lester,' William said, 'I only deliver the best. You won't empty that hole, try how you may — it'll keep filling.' Hubert, Harry, Sid and all others there, crowding to see, wondered how a small, pale village man like Will Cubbage could be given such a strange power. Perhaps the spring was one discovered by Bone long ago when he decided that in that unusual spot he could make a pond?

The water in the two communal wells back in the village fell worryingly low, but that in the Weir yard hardly diminished. Word went round, 'There's water still down at the Wire' and very soon the yard had visitors carrying pails, saying to Sally, 'Well, here I am, Mrs Chapman, come a-begging, only a few pumpings, if none of you mind,' or, 'How-do, Mr Blindell, you won't mind, will you? Just one bucketful, for the tea-kettle and my old man's wash when he gets home — dusty work this dratted weather,' and another, to Granny at the pump-handle, 'Always said this is the best water in Claydon, Mrs Hughes.'

'One bucket the same as the rest, Hetty Haines. You'll have to try with your other bucket somewhere else,' Granny said. As a level-ful pail was carefully carried away, she added, 'A grasper that one. Nobody can heap water up, or she would.' Everyone laughed, then one said, 'Will Hughes, your missis will be after you to find her a lock and chain for this handle,' to which Will solemnly replied, 'Right enough and it don't pay to cross her, not in any way.'

People came daily and the yard children gathered to them instantly, for they brought gossip and tales startling to young ears. At one clustering round the pump, the handle at rest in Granny's hand, there were murmurs of alarm and laughter mixed, to, 'Oh, you don't say! Well, I'm not surprised,' and then, 'Dear me — is that true? Something awful will come of it before long,' and again, 'What can his poor missis do if she daren't lock it away? Anyway, he has to have it to shoot rabbits.'

Hubert privately pressed Sally with the question, *'What* are the *Blue Devils?'* 'Not unearthly creatures, nothing like that,' she answered, put-out for once — 'just a way of speaking about an illness.'

'Illness? — a *blue* sort of illness?' he pressed again.

'Oh, go away and play, boy,' Sally said, for once thoroughly exasperated, 'You children are hearing more than is good for you.'

The yard's new liveliness sent quite wild speculations through young heads when they got together to share them, while dwelling upon their well's acknowledged, clear superiority over all others in the great drought.

It ended at the end of August in heavy thunderstorms, with huge hail-stones and pelting rain, thrashing new pond-water into a sea of froth, bringing with it the pungent smell which rises from parched earth at such times. This raised the happy cry, 'Praises be! It's saying the land is grateful. Joyful we are to be half-drowned at last!'

In the one-room Wesleyan chapel adjoining the Cross Tree and before a full Sunday congregation, Claydon's lay-preacher rose to give thanks as thunder continued to roll, lightning flashed and huge rain-spots spattered the window.

'We thank Thee, O Lord,' he began and then his voice was lost in a sudden drumming on the roof and on that a brilliant lightning-flash lit up the room's whole interior and the rows of alarmed faces. With that came a cannon-like thunder-crash, which brought Jack Wain, in the front row, to his feet, crying, 'Dear Lord, save us! We ent done anything so very special bad. I might have — ' and then came another crash which silenced poor Jack, who sat down, head in hand, in an attitude of prayer, as did most of the congregation.

As the thunder rolled away and the drumming rain eased, the preacher, standing tall all through, spoke once more, 'We thank Thee, Lord, for Thy blessed rain. We'll put up with the other' and then, directly and pointedly, to the rows below him, 'The Lord don't do things by halves when he sets His mind to it.' This, though, he said with a hint in his tone that it should not be over done, continuing that it was not for the likes of Jack Wain to question the way God's gifts come to us when most wanted, in this case the blessed water they had all prayed for only last Sunday. As the worshippers hurried home, the rain now steady and the thunder remote, their thoughts dwelt more on the beneficence of water than on Jack Wain's tantalising 'I might have — ,' although, Claydon being Claydon, it would not be long before some among them would invite him — for his own peace of mind, of course — to complete it.

The Weir re-filled and breezes returned to ruffle the new water. The martins' broods were as large and as agile as their parents. Soon all would be gone. 'Autumn's just round the corner' first one fruit-gatherer would say and another, 'Lovely rain — good job it's stopped, though, for all this to be done and the rest of the harvest to be got in.'

Hubert, and sometimes Harry, sat above the waves again to ride while the travelling was good. Children can sense when something very special is nearing its end. Autumn would see the boys land-lubbers just like Sid, so it is likely that both managed a circumnavigation of the globe before the martins, twittering still, departed. Old and young together, they left their summer residences in good repair, open again to vacant possession, although on short lease.

All but one or two of Misilda's ducks had left too, silenced one by one, to be seen featherless in a wicker-basket under a clean white cloth and carried one by one, by young Billy Giles out into the village. The guinea-fowls had surrendered their high perches to the owls, most also having gone to destinations whence there is no coming back. 'We miss the silly creatures, somehow,' Sally said.

When cold mists lay over the pond and early frosts brought the tree-leaves down over the water the moor-hens disappeared and if one or two water wagtails stayed for a while tripping daintily along the verge they soon took dipping flight and left too. The pond fell so silent that when a single owl screeched it was awesome to the point of alarm. If the children were then in bed it would be heads right under the bed-clothes to be there should he cry again. Hubert did not help by saying in muffled tones, 'Some people say it's not an owl at all — it's a wandering ghost from hundreds of years ago, looking for its old home and this is an old house, isn't it?' By comparison a proper 'too-whit-too-woo' sort of owl was almost a comfort.

Winter was coming. Would the pond freeze over enough to bear you? Last year it did not. George then had said, 'While Tom Giles's horses can break the ice to drink it is not safe for you to get on it' and Sally had exclaimed, 'Dear me, no — do you think I want you running home like that silly Jed Price? I should think he had a lesson for everybody with his breeches full of water from being too daring!' Last year saw no slides except on frozen puddles on the roads, or on crowded patches in the asphalt play-grounds at school.

Christmas drew near and biting winds raised cautious hope. When they fell the pond froze from bank to bank in one night and stayed frozen. The frost strengthened even during the day and grew bitter at night. Tom and Billy brought axes to make a drinking-place for the farm-horses. Harry, Hubert, Sid and a crowd of other boys, girls too, sped straight from school to take to the ice, shouting with glee, 'She bears — she bears, the pond bears. Come right on,' venturing cautiously on. Farm-men came and tested too and the boys explored far over to the field end to survey the exciting scene from there.

Sally had to rattle a tea-tray with a spoon to announce tea-time, as darkness fell.

'The ice is ever so glibby,' Hubert said. 'It's just like glass. Dick Wheeler fell backwards and made a white star on the ice with his head!'

'He won't be troubled,' Sally said. 'He would need to go down twice to have any effect. Wheelers' heads are hard. Just look how the logs are burning — blue flames for another hard frost tonight.'

After tea George said, 'All dress up warm and come outside with me to see something you'll remember.' They stood with him in the darkness in the garden waiting, the air still and bitingly cold.

'You have to wait for it,' he said. 'Keep looking past the Cross Tree, over the village, East Claydon way, where Charley's Wagon and the North Star are, and look how they're twinkling tonight.' They stood gazing, shivering a little for Sally to ask, after a time, 'Well, George, what are we to see?' and at that moment it happened. The whole northern sky slowly changed to a pale spreading glow and the stars suddenly went dim. Then it faded, then lit up again, then faded right away for the stars to shine once more for a full minute. Then, beginning low down, there began a brighter, trembling glow which spread quickly upwards until almost overhead, a curious wavering light reflected on all the upturned faces. It continued to tremble, then stopped, for a great even glow to lighten the whole sky. Then, slowly, it sank right away to leave a darkness blacker than ever with only the stars in it.

'There you are,' George said, 'the Northern Lights. The frost will last — it's creeping south. That's what it means.'

The children clung together. 'We don't like them,' they said, 'let's go in before they start again. What makes them?'

'If I knew I would tell you,' George said, 'I only know it bodes bitter weather. In we go.'

They were only too ready to return to the glow of lamp- and fire-light and the sparkle of Christmas decorations indoors, but they took with them the thrilling thought — at last a Christmas of frost and perhaps — who could tell? — of snow too!

When put to bed Hubert did not sleep. From the pond came distant sounds of jollity, cries and the barking of dogs, darkness adding to the excitement there, but after silence at last prevailed he still fought sleep. Worrying, his head clear of the bed-clothes, he listened. Would 'the sound' come? George had said that in the previous night-hours he had heard the pond-ice split and that now the ice at the drinking hole was four inches thick and the frost increasing it would be bound to split again — 'like a pistol-shot it was,' he said. Would it come? What would it be like? When would it come? He held the bed-clothes to put them instantly over his head. The night-air chilled his hands, the desire for warmth and sleep grew with every moment and the faint window-light, which had been steady for so long, began to rise and fall with the nodding of his head. Then it came — he sat up straight in bed — a double sound, yes, like a gun-shot and its echo and then a sort of fleeting whistle as the ice yielded from bank to bank, then utter silence. Awed, he sat for a moment, listening still. Nothing more came. He sank beneath the bed-clothes. He had heard the strange, eerie thing. Tomorrow Harry and Sid would join him in tracking the split right across from frozen bank to frozen bank — not so worrying after all when you understood that the ice must swell, must have room. But suppose you stood alone on the ice in the middle of the night, with only the stars giving you light, and then, without warning, it happened right under your feet — well, no thank you! He pushed further down into the warmth of the bed and drew the clothes completely over his head.

School ended and each day a laughing, sliding, tumbling crowd gathered before the Weir cottages. Older people tried their skating again and young Arthur Guntrip came to do wonderful figures-of-eight to much cheering, while beginners on wobbly steel invited sudden entanglements and caused them next instant, scoring long scars on the ice with cries of, 'Sorry, I can't stop. I'm into the bank again,' and, 'Oh-oh-oh! Look out for me. Why did I start this. Twice I've been down!'

It went on long after the children's bed-times each evening. 'Like a fair,' Harry Blindell said, grumbling, 'simple pleasures for simple people,' but George dissented, 'Wonderful chance for people to get together Harry. It will last over Christmas now, for sure. Tom Giles threw out ice six inches thick at the water-hole today.'

On Christmas Eve, the sky cloudless and the sun sinking behind the Bernwood farm-house and orchard-trees, men hung storm-lanterns in the low branches of the trees which over-hung the pond and on this the Chapmans and the Blindells pulled their window-curtains far back to reveal their lamp-light, paper lanterns and twinkling Christmas decorations. The children went into their teas in an excited clamour for permission to return to the ice, 'because,' they said, 'it's Christmas Eve and everybody will be there' and because it was Christmas Eve, and the most promising ever for fun by lantern-light beneath the stars, permission was given. Sally said, 'I'm going out myself — its the chance of a life-time, but we must all come in straight after the band has been — for the preparations.'

'Oh yes, for the preparations, the stockings and everything — yes, all that and the band — we'd forgotten the band,' the children cried, dancing round the table. George was a player in it, the band which had given such a startling account of itself on Sally's wedding-day, which would play in the village first and then in the yard and at the farm, as always on Christmas Eve and never before in such winterly weather.

As the children sought fellow-sliders in the strange light over the pond George set out along the lane with his instrument under his arm, meeting and greeting village people drawn to the ice and the conviviality already bubbling there, where soon the company was such that skaters gave up and became sliders, or venturers to the old pond's furthest recesses, with many 'Oohs' and laughter. There was no moon but a multitude of stars and the air bitterly cold. The swaying lanterns cast peculiar shadows over the moving figures who slid and joked, clung to each other and solemnly declared that the Wire, for once in a while, was doing Claydon proud. Those who were long past skating, or even sliding, vowed that they must at least stand on the ice, if only just on, saying, well they declared, it was something they had not done since they were children and not ever on a Christmas Eve, saying that whoever put the lanterns in the trees was inspired and that Claydon would remember it all for many a long day. And then — hark! Was that the band starting up in the village? 'What a night — it's hard to see who's who,' a voice struck up in the darkness and next, 'Hullo, is this Jesse Newman I see? Fancy you venturing out, Jesse.' Through the cold air came an old man's trembling tones, 'Not since I was a boy has there been a Christmas do like this. I had to come, case they play on the ice, the band, I mean.'

At this Harry, Hubert and Sid, standing by, decided to make for the Cross Tree to listen. Away in the village *'Once in Royal — '* was ending, so they stood together waiting, saying nothing, to judge for themselves the band's progress. Minutes passed and then came, in the near distance, the tread of heavy feet and, after another pause, *'Christians awake — '* always the opening piece. 'That's it,' Harry said, 'they're at the Post Office, I reckon. Come on, back to the pond to be ready for 'em. Dare you to stand on that deep part where there's no lanterns.' And there, away from the noisy crowd, they stood for a full half-minute in awe on the untouched ice, treacherously smooth, heavy darkness overhead, mysterious blackness under their feet. It had been a boy's dare — no-one would dare say he wouldn't. 'Right then' Hubert said, 'see if we can find where the moor-hen had her nest, over the other side.' Groping, Harry and Hubert had to feel for it, flattened and be-draggled in the brittle reeds and at that moment came the tramp of feet at the Cross Tree.

'Band's coming, boys!' shouted Sid, 'get to 'em' and together they slid, staggered and ran, pushing through the crowd, all now edging forward to clap the men, the boys joining the troupe of children at their heels.

Jackie, the band-master, led, Jimmy Warner with the drum and Slipper Price, bearing pole and lantern, were at the rear. People closely followed as Jackie marshalled his men to the bank in the angle of the cottages, which surely must have brought them piquant memories, for again the Chapmans' door was open wide, the adjacent windows crowded, as lamp-light softly outlined the watchers and touched the men and their brass as they stood to play. Every person there was known, so jollity, smiles and much rallying Jackie saying, 'Well, here we are again, folks, and a Merry Christmas say we to one and all.' He was quite grey now and a little bowed, but his grin was just as before. Jimmy was diminished as ever behind the drum and Slipper, even more uncertain with the lantern, had become almost a shadow. The other members were much as before — George, first baritone; his father George, Hubert's grandfather, tenor horn; Jesse Carter, second cornet; Joe Hamp, second baritone; 'Zachar' Norman, euphonium – all as before, except the railway-porter, trombone, who had been promoted signal-man 'up the line', that is, to Watford Junction. This elevated young man blasted amongst them no more, which, many thought, was no great disadvantage.

Grouped around Slipper and his lantern they eased their brass keys and blew on their fingers, while Jimmy gently tapped the drum, looking to Jackie for his signal.

'Are you ready, men?' he said, his cornet raised. 'Never have we seen such a gathering. Show 'em all what we can do. It'll be after four,' but as all drew breath, there came a loud call from the ice, 'Come on, men — for once in a lifetime stand on the old pond to glorify us. It bears — it'ud bear Sanger's Circus!' and on this came cheers, laughter and urgent clapping and from Jackie, 'Hold up men. What about it? It's never been done before as I know. Let's make history. I'll lead. Somebody steady Slipper,' and so with forebodings about the lantern and the drum they made their way down to the ice to edge carefully on it and to settle right below Sally's front-room window.

'Keep close to 'em, boys,' Hubert urged, and he, Sid and Harry moved close behind George as sliders, skaters, onlookers, all other children and dogs crowded to them in a buzz of delight, apprehension and doubt, for Slipper's lantern swayed ominously and Jimmy and the drum at first lost their bearings. When all was settled Jackie once more called, 'Are you ready men? Better not full power, seeing where we stand — nice and full, though and, Jimmy, light on the drum. You'd never forgive yourself if you put us all through this ice.' Laughter followed that but then almost a silence as he said, 'After four, then' and then full and steady in the night air came *'Christians awake, salute the Happy Morn — '* many beginning to sing as the dogs fled away into the shadows. The lanterns swayed in the trees, Slipper's light flickered on the men's faces and vibrating horns, stars, countless in number, twinkled overhead, shadows slowed down and stopped as people stood to sing. Voices, thin and clear in the frosty air, rose and fell quite movingly in their strange setting. Right behind George, Hubert, Sid and Harry sang as they had never sung before, the first verse, that is — the rest had to be powerful humming. Joining-in was absolutely the compelling thing — the throb of the music, everyone around you in full throat, the sense of history being made called for a full contribution and 'where would they all be,' thought Hubert, 'without my Dad and my up-the-village Gramp?'

When it came to '*While Shepherds watched* — ' the old tune was demanded. It's a tune as should never get lost, never be let to die,' declared Joe Hamp, lowering his shining piece in order to give voice — 'Oh, it's a powerful tune. Let's put it to 'em, Jackie,' and, with the band striking up, he led with fierce purpose from the first note: '*While shep-herds wa-atched their flo-ocks by night, all seated on the ground, all sea-e-e-eated on the ground, The angel o-o-f the Lor-or-ord came down and glowry shone around and glowry shone around and glow-owry shone around.*' Joe made a big thing of the glories, his head thrown back, his eyes shining, his beard pointing to the stars through every verse.

Jesse Newman stood close against him nodding his head and smiling and when the last notes died he piped up to say, 'Glad tidings if you like — what a night this is! Never since I was a boy — . Help me to get back, will you? Frez right over for the men to play on it — wonderful! Don't let me slip down, get me to the side. You sang well, Joe — you sang how it allus ought to be sung. I shall go to me bed contented and to me last 'un, come to that.' Willing hands guided him home. After '*Hark the Herald* — ' the band moved off and soon were heard at Bernwood, their sounds echoing joyfully in the courtyard. Lesters would regale them, as always, with mulled ale and mince-pies, so there would be the usual encore, the lugubrious '*Mistletoe-bough*', to which Hubert, when safely indoors, would again demand the full story. The pond now rapidly cleared — there were special things to be done indoors before bed-time. Hubert, faithfully there for those things, heard the tramp and the jolly chatter of the bandsmen as they returned along the lane to tour down-the-village, Sid and Harry with them to the last.

Through Christmas Day the pond had its sheet of ice entirely to itself in a strange quietness and curious emptiness and in the evening light snow began to fall. 'The wind is getting up in the soft quarter,' George said, 'we shall have a fall' and a fall there was in the night, so that on Boxing Day morning the children woke to a white world in which a smooth gleaming whiteness lay over the whole of the pond. Although they were quickly out making snow-balls, happy in a sudden new wonder, none ventured to disturb that whiteness. Pausing in their play, they gazed at its wide stretch of unsullied carpet as if a beautiful curtain had been drawn over a fantastical play, or dream.

BERNWOOD FARM AND FOREST

Bernwood Forest covered wide tracts of Oxfordshire and Buckinghamshire for centuries. Bernwood Farm and the adjoining Weir are little more than a dozen miles from the county boundaries over which it spread. Only fragments of the forest remained or an occasional gaunt oak standing isolated in a home park.

If they had thought about it at all the Weir children would have decided, without a second of doubt, that the Claydon woods had been the heart of the forest, for 'our woods', as they called them, were not negligible. Runts and Belmoor Woods covered the southern end of their familiar hill, Great Sea Wood lay away westward at its foot and Home, Curtis's and Grendon Woods continued beyond that. From Home Wood the squire's people drew their cord-wood along a made road a mile long, as straight as a ruler.

Beyond the woods lay and lies Otmoor, a placid almost sleepy countryside, in which is a small area of wild plant-life called Bernwood to this day, where, the great trees all gone, the snake-like fritillaries bloom and nod along with other survivals from the past.

The old squire had made certain that the name of the forest should not be lost in Claydon when he built his new show-farm, taking away the acreage which, presumably, had first been the mysterious Bone's, when he transformed the timber-frame farm-house and dairy into cottages. There and then came young Benjamin Hornby to be Bernwood's first tenant farmer, preceding the Lesters. For the younger people of the village he had now become a shadowy figure, a subject of old men's reminiscences, little else.

'F.W. LESTER & SONS, BERNWOOD FARM, BOTOLPH CLAYDON, BUCKS' proclaimed the yellow-painted farm-wagons of the second-generation tenants. The wagons were built, painted and lettered by Harry's father, Leonard Wiggins, in his wheel-wright's shop, up-the-village, the iron-work for them beaten, shaped, finished and fixed by Harry's Uncle Herb Wiggins, who had the smithy next door.

Fred Lester, long called 'Gobbler' from his manner of speech, was respected for his well-managed mixed farming and prize-winning cattle, horn and hoof. Three of his grown-up sons worked the same hours as the hired men, intending to be farmers themselves. He was kindly enough in a bluff fashion and invariably claimed that he had started many a village lad towards a good way of life on the land. Hubert's father and grandfather and other men worked many years for him, some for fifty years, outliving him in the end.

Whether they were aware of it or not, his family were all Weir people in the eyes of the village and of many farther off, completing the community, along with their fetlocked shires, Emily, the chestnut cob, and her companion, Polly, the donkey, the milking Shorthorns and Bertie the bull, while Jock the Old-English sheep-dog and the turkey-cock considered the paddock to be their personal territory. They stood up for the rights of all. Villagers, delivery-men and strangers were announced with heavy growls, suspicious sniffings, a tail fanned out, wing-tips pressed hard to the ground, wattles aflame. Otherwise Jock was a nuzzling body-wagging hearth-rug and the turkey-cock a daintily circling parading braggart, his gobble-gobble-gobble going through most of the day.

In season and out of season the farm-men spent most of their waking hours on the Bernwood land. Harry, Hubert and Sid knew them and their ways to a man, followed the progress of their sowing, reaping, stack-building, foddering, shearing, hedge-trimming and laying, listening often to their tales, believing or half-believing, but never quite disbelieving.

'Now, let me see,' side-whiskered Arthur Webb, George's fellow herdsman and friend, began in slow careful fashion as he and other hay-makers rested arms and wooden rakes after an hour of non-stop swath-turning — 'it was in Hornby's time when the new nag, down at the Lawn Farm, ran away with the milk float, taking the London milk to the station for the six o' clock train. Judge had only just bought the critter cheap up in London — she was never much good to him. A chap they called Jimmy Shanks was a-driving. They ended up in the station-yard with the nag sitting in the shafts, half-mad trying to get up, and this Jimmy sitting in the milk as never got anywhere near London. Trouble followed that Jimmy wherever he went — married a wench from t'other side of Granborough. He should have got to know more about her folk and her before wedding-bells. Things got serious with 'em pretty quick — ' and then Arthur stopped, realising the absorbed attention of the three young listeners, to say next, 'Go and do whatever you were a-doing, you young-uns — raking-out along the hedge, weren't you? I'm talking to George and Billy,' so the young-uns withdrew, deprived, as the boys thought, of the best bit.

'Yes,' continued Arthur, 'taking clothes out of shops in Aylesbury and selling 'em round Bicester way, that was the first thing and Jimmy made out a receiver. They both got put away for it. Then there was the ginger-headed babby that come on the scene, Jimmy threw her out on that — he was as black as a raven. Claydon was best without 'em when they went, first her and then him. Well, men — we must start again.'

On another day Ben Norman rested his scythe to say, 'The rinder-pest? What was it like? What have you heard about it? God save us from that, boy — all that digging we had to do for to bury the poor things and the police standing over us all the time and one fine milker after another pole-axed and tumbled into the pit till every last cow was in and old Judge stamping about and swearing and his missis and the gals with their aprons over their heads, so as they shouldn't see, and crying their eyes out. It don't bear thinking about. I was only a boy-chap at the time but I remember it clear as day. — Where were they buried? Why, in Curtis's Ground, nigh to where Beckett's be now at the Lawn Farm, where Judge was.'

Making a visit to the flat field at the foot of the hill the boys gazed in puzzlement on the ten acres of bearded wheat bending gently to the June breeze.

'I don't believe it,' said Sid firmly.

'Well, old Ben said so and he ent a liar,' Hubert observed.

'All them buried bones,' Harry said — 'my Dad says it's true. People went to the work-house because of it.'

They turned on that sobered and quiet, to climb back up the Balloon Field for home, though with some delay there because men said a real balloon had once landed in the trees at the top; but the trees, catching the breeze, had nothing to say about it so a race through the Clump Furland and Middle Ground helped, for a few moments at least, to banish thoughts of that terrible murrain of beasts and of what lay beneath the waving corn in Curtis's Ground. Ben milked ten or a dozen cows twice a day at the Middle Ground cow-shed which, at a gallop, they passed. He was a master-man with a scythe when leading the mowers to cut a 'road' round twenty acres of ripe oats, barley or wheat so that the flailing reaper could be put in to begin the reaping, Tom Giles driving, Old Brownie pulling and the machine kicking out the bound sheaves one by one. At the day's end men and boys would stay until the last were made to stand in stooks of six or eight in lines stretching from hedge to hedge, where the hardening of the grain would complete over several days and field-mice and birds enjoy a brief happiness until the wagons arrived for the picking-up.

When rain put a stop to work in the hay or corn Ben took charge of the boys who had been put to thistle-cutting in the rough pastures. They used sickles as he chopped and swept with his scythe. He allowed no tom-foolery with these edge tools: 'Play the fool if you like when the tools be put safe when we break off for a rest and a bite — I don't mind it then, so long as you don't do damage, or break your necks.' He was a tolerant mentor and insisted on the countryman's pace for all field-work — 'so's you've got summat left at the end of the day.' He knew best how to corner a rabbit in a clump of stinging-nettles and then how to 'put him to sleep comfortable, like that' — the back-hand blow behind the ears — 'the next one goes to which of you cuts most thistles by home-time.' He imparted much non-school knowledge of a useful sort most days.

He wore a long-sleeved waistcoat all the year round; his corduroy trousers were strapped below the knees and he favoured the out-moded front flap to the trousers, which fascinated and amused the boys when it came into use behind a rick, or clump of hedge-thorns — 'Go a bit further along, boy, if you must go,' he urged. The same flat, battered hat served him through all seasons. He wore no whiskers on his solemn jowls, which were eternally bristled. When searching for a thought he passed a hand over them he drew forth a small rasping sound echoing the swish of his scythe felling corn. Any of the boys would willingly turn the grind-stone for him in the Bernwood cart-shed where he honed the finest possible edge on the scythe. 'It's got to be sharp like a razor,' he said, 'turn steady, boy, and we must keep the stone wet, then the blade 'ull be whetted proper. You could cut a lawn with this now — they had to in the old days. Sheep were too messy for grand lawns.' He kept his sharpening rubber in a slotted leather loop in his belt at the back. When keeping the edge in the field the ringing tones along the blade went to a tune recognisably his and his alone. 'Hark,' one would say, 'Ben's sharping agen. He's cut along the headland a'ready.' 'A valuable man,' said Lester, 'dependable.'

So too was Jesse Carter the Bernwood rick-builder. No matter whether of hay, corn-sheaves, bouncy clover or loose straw from the threshing, his stacks stood straight and true and when harvest was done he tidied, topped and thatched them himself. A man of parts, cornet in the village band, he led the church choir, singing in ringing thirds below the top-line in hymn, psalm and response.

'What would we do without you, Mr Carter?' the Rector would say. 'Well, sir,' Jesse replied, 'the others take a bit o'keeping in line, they do, speaking the truth, but I don't let 'em wander. I keep hold on 'em, first note to Amen.' 'You do, you do and you do it admirably,' and the Rector would again pat Jesse's arm, wondering what in the world he would do without those commanding thirds, Sunday after Sunday. Jesse's small quizzical face, bearing an unusually wispy moustache for those days of the grand walrus variety, twitched happily at such appreciation of his musicality. He went away humming the Doxology. When in his later years he grew too unsteady for rick-building George succeeded him as builder and shaper, but not without close, suspicious supervision for at least two seasons and autumn visits after that, 'to see how Lester's ricks stand — not so bad, George — not so bad.'

Arthur Webb, George Chapman, Ben Norman, Jesse Carter, Tom Giles the carter and Will 'Mutton' the shepherd, were typical of the time and George's father, Hubert's grandfather also George Chapman was another. A character known well beyond the village, he was called 'Brassie' since his boyhood, from a brief passion for horse-brasses. He took in hand for Lester the succession of milch-cows who 'dried-off', or were 'barreners', who kept diminishing milk in the tips of their horns, as he put it. His work centred on the Old House in the village, with its cow-shed, bull-pen and rickyard, which the Lesters had occupied before Bernwood and continued to use. The farm-house had become the village post-office. Some people living nearby went to Brassie daily to buy their household milk, which they took away frothy, uncooled and sometimes with a stray bit of chaff in it. There he pointed out to Hubert, who was on a milk errand for lame Mrs Rodwell, that the first squirtings of milk from a cow's udder into the metal pail pronounced the word 'mon-key'. One absorbed knowledge readily from such a discerning man. Naturally, Hubert stood to listen and have it proved. Brassie's mutton-chop whiskers gave him an old-fashioned look but he regularly kept up with the times. When the new Sunday newspaper, the News of the World, first came to Claydon he took it at once, animated by the promise of its title, to supplement his 'dailies'. After a few issues he cancelled his order, disillusioned. He was proud to have been elected the first chairman of the Parish Council and he continued to compile his personal spelling-book, started then, 'Take the difference between 'vitals' and 'victuals', he said, 'it could trap you and make you look a fool'.

Hubert soon realised that he had an unusual man for a grandfather — not only a Parish Councillor but also tenor-horn in the village band that met each Sunday morning in his barn for practice. He was purveyor of the mild beer essential to smooth rehearsal there, and also, because of his rich baritone voice, a man on call for the concerts and socials held in the village hall. There, piano accompaniment scorned, vintage songs like 'The Old Arm-Chair' were given, note and word perfect, with no faltering and head held high. It was something to have a 'Gramp' in such demand, who could command an audience and win cries of: 'Good old Brassie — encore!' a countryman to the core and of unabashed liveliness and humour, yet given to sudden seriousness, saying one minute, 'I've seen more people carried feet first out of these villages than are living in them now,' in the next providing an earthy tale. He was not of the Weir, but the Weir claimed him by right of family. Also he, George Chapman, Senior, brought the unsold Old House milk by yoke and buckets daily to the Bernwood dairy.

That the Bernwood animals firmly belonged became clear when Tom Giles and his son Billy prepared Young Brownie and her foal and the promising gelding for the agricultural show at Buckingham or Aylesbury, Tring or distant Peterborough. The children stood at the stable-door to see the washing, combing, polishing, plaiting and be-ribboning and followed as they set out, Tom and Billy marvellously smartened men, holding brand-new halters, and, at the Cross Tree, gave them three cheers as they turned downhill for the railway-station. With laughing gossiping others they gathered there again for the return, anxious to see what rosettes and award-cards they bore. Rows of these adorned the roof-beams above the stalls in the stables where the winners and highly-commendeds champed oats, stamped feet in satisfaction after a long drink at the pond and a comforting rub-down, or just slept standing up.

In spring Tom's family entertained the perky little groom with the white cravat, riding-breeches and gleaming gaiters, who brought the stallion called The Entire to be stabled at the Old House, or, sometimes, at Bernwood. His huge combed fetlocks, mane and tail seemed too fancily crimped for his bulk. His snorting little neigh always spelt danger and he was given the centre of the road wherever the little groom led him. Each year he, or his like, came to Claydon, or how could there have been a Young Brownie as well as steady Old Brownie and the engaging young foal going off to a show, frisky as a puppy and the same gingery-brown as her mother and grandmother and with grandma's white star on her forehead, the very same?

House-routine at the Bernwood farm-house revolved around wash-days. Once a month long lines of sheets, table-cloths, towels and vital garments were strung out on the paddock to billow and flap, sending the turkey-cock and his hens to its farthest limits and the pony and donkey almost as far. It appeared to be supervised by Mrs Lester's companion-help, an elegant lady who wore no uniform, not even an apron, but a dark sober dress and so was said to be superior. The 'teen-age general-help staggered out with laundry-baskets, twice her size, while Miss Hall carried the pegs and set the sails for something like a river regatta. The Weir children gazed in wonder at the size of it and took some interest when later, for a brief while, Hubert's favourite aunt became the general-help. Sally's youngest sister, sixteen-year-old Amy from Bucknell Lodge Farm, Hubert's summer-holiday paradise, was too high-spirited for all that confronted her in that demanding and crowded household, where there were two grim ladies all set to train such as she for 'proper service'. Her bicycle-bell would jangle shrilly as she sped past the Weir cottages careering along the lane and away, heading for the Post Office or for Webbs' general store on an errand; or to the White House, or the vicarage at East Claydon, with a brace of Aylesbury ducks, oven-ready, which she herself had plucked but not, of course, dressed and prepared. Daily she kicked against the pricks. She had so many of the desired qualities, if only her exuberance could be subdued — the right presence, bright clear speech and enough good looks, but sadly she lacked deference, would toss her head and advance opinion. Invariably she looked in on Sally when returning from her errands breathless and laughing, as she related 'the latest at the house', mimicking exactly the tones of the last injunction, 'I'm giving you no more than ten minutes there and back, my girl, and see you have the exact right change. There will be no time for back-chat with anybody.'

Amy, so full of life, who busy though she was, made time to engage in all the yard children's liveliness, suddenly was gone.

'I am not putting up with it, Sally,' she had said.

'Nor need you,' Sally agreed. 'Give quiet, proper notice and leave them to find somebody made of putty. Then they'll be all smiles. You can do better than be at such beck and call.'

For Hubert and all the other yard children her going was like the sudden covering of the noon-day sun by a single great wandering cloud on a summer's day.

Rick-yard, granary, stables, cart-sheds, cow-sheds, the foaling-box, the children explored them all. The hay and corn stacks were built, thatched, cut and threshed almost at their doors. The visiting steam corn-thresher vied with the treadle sewing-machine, for they puffed and stitched at times within yards of each other. Hubert and Harry, sometimes also Sid, searched for artfully concealed hens' nests in nettle-clumps and brambles and for the odd carelessly laid single egg in a manger, or corn-bin, or the bed of an idle wagon, to win from Mrs Lester a rare smile, from Miss Hall, 'Thank you, child,' but from 'Missilda' a slice of fruit-cake, milk or lemonade.

Forty-odd years after its building Bernwood Farmhouse still looked new in its solid red brick, but the old farm kept a strong grip in the thoughts of the older men who had known it, who spoke as if the old-time farming would never be usurped however much Lester's sons urged him towards a side-delivery rake for the hay and a mechanical loader and for a Friesian bull to supersede the Shorthorn. The children, listening to the men's talk, decided that they were born to a clear inheritance and so could go wherever they wished. Indeed, Bone himself could have slept in Hubert's bedroom when it was new, could have known the pattern of its wall and ceiling beams, just as the Chapman children saw them, much darkened now and hard as iron but the joists pegged, not nailed, as he had left them.

Lona and her sister Alice gathered dandelion heads near home and cowslips farther afield for Granny's winemaking, while Hubert, Harry and Sid explored as far as the woods to see what they might see and to do what came into their heads provided they broke no hedges, remembered the dictum about field-gates, skirted growing crops and walked quietly past in-lamb ewes and heifers in their season. They knew the remote hedgerow corners where white violets grew, the stretch of verdant ditch where yellow archangels shone in a tangle of star-like stitchwort and pink ragged robins, and the place alongside the road to the woods where, shyly withdrawn amongst brambles and dogwood, the strangeness of spindle-berries was an enticement to push in to test their squashy pink lobes. They went often to the field called Cuckoo where purple orchises grew because a small stream ran through it. In the growing season there they tasted the wild water-cress, not much liking it without bread-and-butter. They called the little orchises 'cuckoos'.

Not for them the rough gated road when they headed for the woods, but grass under-foot all the way — first through Home Ground where the milking-cows lay solemnly chewing the cud declining to move; then into the sloping grass-stretch of the Breach, with a pause at the warren there, startling the nibbling rabbits back like quick-silver into their holes; next across the flat 'Lawn', where fine yearling shires looked up and then went on with their grazing and so to the Clump Furland, down to swedes but with a good grass verge, and finally into the Pightle, the rough piece next to Runts, the first of the woods. There, never-failing, a sharp-eyed wood-pigeon would announce their arrival by a noisy clattering away through the tree-branches for safety farther in.

One morning they climbed the gate at the wood's entrance for a rest and a look around, then ventured in to cut straight, slim hazel wands for bows and arrows, which were plentiful and springy from the coppicing of two winters back. After the departure of the noisy pigeon the wood was eerily quiet until they heard a distant gate close and then the approach of foot-steps through the trees — Jack Carter, head game-keeper, who need not be feared. On he came, a strong plodding figure with a gun under his arm, great side-pockets, heavy boots, leather leggings and as always, a blue jay's feather in his hat-band. He stood before them leaning on his long stick.

'Well,' he said, 'what's troubling you?'

'Nothing really,' Hubert said, 'bows and arrows, that's all. We don't want to go into the wood, do we, Harry — do we, Sid?'

'No,' those two said together, 'we only came for these.'

'Cut what you want,' Carter said, 'there's plenty. The squirrels will plant more. This won't be thinned out again till you've growed up and earning your livings. And who do I see? — Biddy Jennings's boy? It's writ all over him and Len Wiggins's and which of all they Chapmans be you? Brassie your Gramp, eh? Don't do all he does, boy. I went to school with him.'

'Thank you,' they said as he turned away saying, 'I know what you said, but the wood draws folks in. Don't get yourselves lost. I shan't come looking for you.' He climbed the gate to go.

They watched him cross to Belmoor Wood until he disappeared into it. 'He's all right,' said Harry ' — for a game-keeper.'

It would have been different in the incubating season when in coops in the ride he had farm-yard hens sitting on clutches of pheasants' eggs. The Pightle was your limit then and if you needed to go through the wood you kept to the road all the way.

As to the road through the wood, it was the way to Fine Moor at the end of the hill and the view to Oxford, twenty miles away, if you were lucky with the weather. It was a branch of the rutted track which began at the bottom of the village, the centuries-old New Road. Could the boys have known two things of that road they would have trodden its length in wonderment from its beginning through to its bosky over-grown end on the far side of Coppice Hill Farm on the left-hand side of the wood. Seth Beckett of the farm used it, as did Fleetwood Tompkins of Fine Moor, for access to the village and the wider world; so did Lester for his farm-work, but it saw few others. It lay silent for days on end — gated, deeply rutted and pot-holed, growing grass between its wheel-tracks. Hubert tackled Ben Norman about it as he mended a gap in the unkempt hedge which bordered its main length, 'Why is it called new? It doesn't look new. People say it's ever so old.'

'So it is,' answered Ben, staying his bill-hook — 'never been called anything different — new once, same as you, name got fixed. Who named it? Bless the boy — how could I know? Dead folk, all forgot and lost out o'mind' — and that had to do from Ben.

Yet, in the muniment-room at Claydon House there is an old estate-map captioned: *A Map of the Parish and Lordship of East Claydon in Buckinghamshire, belonging to Right Honourable Lord Fermanagh, Measur'd and Mapt in Year of Our Lord 1742, by me, John Lee.* John Lee, of Aylesbury had done a painstaking survey, no doubt on behalf of the rent-roll, and he shows the road clearly, just as Botolph Claydon people still know it, running from the bottom end of the village, through the gated stretch where Ben gave his views, next passing Runts Wood on the left and then Coppice Hill Farm and after that on to the map's edge. It is plainly marked along its length: *Coach Road to Grendon Underwood.* Adjoining that quiet village lies Grendon Wood. That and the village are no more than four miles, as the crow flies, from the boys' homes in Claydon.

Could they have known about the old coach road as they perched on the Pightle gate whittling their arrows, what would not have welled up in their imaginations? One hears pounding hooves, iron tyres crunching stones, the swish and crack of a long whip, the imperative winding of a horn, sees a commanding coachman in a great cloak, swaying passengers, a gleaming coach, wheels muddied with travel. The road is well-made, if a little rough, and there is a plunging of hooves at the turn into the village for the uphill pull past first Sid's and then Harry's front-gardens, the horn bringing all down-the-village folk out to see, wave, and to time their clocks. But there is no stopping, even at the Cross Tree. The left-hand turn there done with a daring swing ensures a straight fast run along the hill-top to East Claydon's twists and turns before the run down-hill to Winslow. After that, who knows? Foreign parts without doubt, should the three boys have been riding. One can see, too, the carrier's wagon drawn aside at the Pightle, or the Cross Tree, or the Winslow turn at East Claydon, for the coach to pass, the driver at his horses' heads, steadying them, as his one or two passengers — of the humbler sorts — stand to wave the speeding ones on.

If only the boys could have known. Instead they sat on the gate's top rail peeling bark and whittling away content with their acquisitions until, in the distance, came a sound of their new century, the long cry of an express train passing through the farther woods aiming for middle England. They sat up, pocketed their knives and collected their weapons.

'Come on, you two,' Hubert said, jumping to the road, 'let's get home. When you hear that it's going to rain. My Dad says so.'

For a second the others stood tall on the gate looking west over Belmoor Wood where, low down, a dark cloud was rising. They too jumped down to the road and all three raced for home.

And if only they could have known one thing more about the old road as they ran, turning to watch the sky, walking, then running again, stopping to retrieve fallen arrows and hurrying again, because the storm-rack was rising fast above the woods, the whole sky darkening. They took the shortest way over the fields and were safely in their homes when the storm broke, the first rain fell and the first thunder rolled. It could not be expected that they would have known, any more than they knew about the coach-road, that Shakespeare may have travelled the New Road, that same coach-road, making for Grendon Underwood, as the sun was lowering at the end of a long summer day long ago.

John Aubrey in one of the briefest of his *Brief Lives* says, 'Mr William Shakespeare lodged there' — that is, at Grendon — 'one night when, but eighteen years of age, or thereabouts, he sought a new life in London to be an actor at one of the play-houses, where he became a man of a very readie pleasant smoothe wit and a writer of plays which took well.'

Aubrey was somewhat of a learned gossip, it must be admitted, and he gave this information late, but it has never been gainsaid. Grendon lies half-way between Stratford and London on a direct route. Shakespeare had about forty miles to do to reach it and most, if not all of it, would have been on foot. Did he then set out in the earliest of all English summer dawns to do that first stretch in one day, needing to rest during the shortest of all summer nights — perchance to dream? For Aubrey says, 'I think it was Midsomer Night that he happened to lye there.' A route from Stratford for that first day's journey takes you straight down Claydon's New Road, the coach-road, for the last few miles before Grendon. No-one knew better than Shakespeare a direct way to anything, including a bed after a day's travel and also, one is bound to agree, to new ideas for plays which might take well. Listen to Aubrey again, 'The Humoure of the Constable in Midsomer Night's Dream he happened to take at Grendon in Bucks' — and of the play itself in Grendon Wood? There is no constable amongst the charming mechanicals in the Dream, who so amused 'the Duke and his Lady on their wedding-day at night', but Peter Quince was to be found in any Bucks village and there is something of him in Dogberry, who, in a bumbling countryman's way, caused right to be done in 'Much Ado about Nothing'.

Never mind John Aubrey's, 'I have been told — ,' his, 'I think I have been told — ,' his, 'I have heard — ,' which, in truth, have a wonderful Claydon ring about them, it takes but a modicum of supposition to have Bully Bottom, Puck, the falling-out of Titania and Oberon, the Mistresses Pease-blossom and Mustard-seed, the distracted lovers and the counterparts of Grendon's, or Claydon's, mummers all in Grendon Wood in the most famous night of magic ever devised. Shakespeare himself and Aubrey give us leave to imagine it.

Hubert, Harry and Sid, like Shakespeare's wanton boys, who swam on bladders near Clopton Bridge, were creatures of the hour. When the storm had passed they met again to experiment in the puddles newly-formed in the lane, orange-peel sought with an urgency all boys can understand. Place a piece, outer-side down, in the shallow water, then grind it hard into the road with the heel of your boot and wait — rainbow colours spread delicately over the surface of the water. It was a brief wonder. Oranges, except at Christmas and a little after, were rarities, so you made the most of your chance to pore over shimmering, changing colours in a muddy lane. They dallied, puzzled over its strangeness, then recollected and sped away to Harry's bench in his father's carpentry-shop up-the-village to work on their bows and arrows with silent concentration.

Bernwood through its seasons, the Weir water and all other accessible ponds, the Old House barn, stables and rick-yard, the road to the woods, the near woods, encompassed their needs. They felt no pull to seek further. They and the yard children generally knew instinctively what could and what should not be done in their country setting. Lively young neighbours, they were fortunate that the Lesters gave them a free run while aware, mostly, of their doings, tolerant with them through their formative years. Their own four sons and Hilda when children not long before, had ranged, explored, scrambled, experimented, damaged themselves on occasion and then recovered in much the same way. Now they were all in a period of change. The three sons, demonstrably committed to farming, constantly prodded their father towards new ways, so that soon all the milking-cows were Friesians milked by machinery, the hay bundled and picked up by it in the fields, his ploughs pulled by tractors with power to turn over the stiffest of Claydon clays. When, in his sixties, he died he travelled to his rest in the church-yard of St Mary's, East Claydon, drawn by Brownie, the last of his shires, in a flower-decked hay-wagon, one of the last made in Claydon, in a picturesqueness regarded by many as quaint, but in a characteristic assertion that if his farming had become out-of-date it had been top-quality from first to last.

Of the boys who had roamed his farm in the days of the yard children, only Sid settled on the land. The others went their different ways in times of increasing change, in which the village changed completely.

The author's home and the Weir Pond in the late 1920's.

The Main Street of Botolph Claydon leading from Bernwood Farm and the Weir to East Claydon in the early years of this century.

*The Cross Tree and village people at Botolph Claydon in the early part of this century.
Postcard: Courtesy of Mrs May Durran of Steeple Claydon.*

*Webbs', the village shop at Botolph Claydon.
Postcard: Courtesy of Mrs May Durran.*

Church Walk, East Claydon. The path along which the band walked for the Club Feast.

East Claydon showing the house said to have once been a coaching inn on the road to Grendon Underwood.

Claydon House and Lake, the front elevation.   *Postcard: Courtesy of Mrs May Durran.*

Claydon House and All Saints' Church showing a tea-party in progress on the lawn beneath the cedar-trees.

Big Oak. Claydon Park.

One of the ancient oaks in the park of Claydon House, perhaps once part of Bernwood Forest.
Postcard: Courtesy of Mrs May Durran.

The author and his elder sister Eva in 1908, taken by travelling photographer Bob Pretty.

CALLERS

Callers were the salesmen who met many of the household needs and some of the desires of the villages and of the scattered homes around. They were horse-drawn in a variety of vehicles built or adapted for their purposes, although several tried the motor engine, with reservations everywhere about any permanent use of such contraptions. The same view was taken of the private motor cars which began to appear, to be designated the fads and fancies of the well-to-do and rich 'show-offs' with more money than sense.

The first equipage completely set aside when young Sir Harry bought a curious steam-car was the landau, with gleaming maroon panels, the family crest of the Big House emblazoned thereon, drawn by glossy, high-stepping horses in harness of high taste with Bradley, the coachman usually far more grandly attired than the passengers.

Rees Rees still depended on his knowing cob to get him home to Knowl Hill Farm on market-days. To have that faithful animal coming down the middle of the street, his master swaying and lost to the world, his whip trailing in the dust, was alarming enough. But mercifully the wise man continued to rely on his four-legged horse-power and mothers to keep their children well behind their front-garden gates at the latter end of a long day.

There were no such alarms when the first callers tried motor power. They were deemed to have sense and care, because of their commodities as well as their persons, but such venturers were few. However they travelled, the in-comers varied widely in character, brought interest, views and news, yarns and often jollity, as well as new lines in washing-powders, scourers, soaps, cake-mixes, materials, ready-mades and vital needs, such as bread, flour and fresh meat.

Bread, the staff of life itself, was baked two miles away by Dickens of Granborough, mostly in the shape of the cottage loaf with flattish base and smaller top knuckled in, small, large or quartern. It was brought to the Yard on Tuesdays and Fridays every week by Tommy Heritage, a smallish grey-haired man of few words whose hooded cart left a yeasty aroma in his wake and whose person was a little floury, because he also carried flour for home baking. 'Bread today, Ma'am?' — his call from the open back-door brought the call, 'Two loaves today, please, Thomas' and two, probably joined, would be placed on the back-kitchen table. In later years on the Friday delivery it could be, 'Three, please, Thomas — one baked brown' and he, 'Ah — so he's coming home for the week-end, is he? Good-day to you, then.'

At the tail-board of his van was a short transverse rope and sometimes slung over that a sack of flour. Unknown to him an agile boy would leap on it for a ride until a passer-by, or other boys, called: 'Whip behind, Tommy. Give the monkey a flip', when the whip would whistle along the van's side but somewhat gently. Although audacious boys might refer to him as Tommy Herring-bone, he was a kindly man whom most folk instinctively addressed fully as Thomas. His service spanned many years.

Two days a week were Claydon days for Colgrove, the Winslow butcher, one for taking orders, Friday or Saturday for delivery. Many households had their own home-cured bacon but there was steady call for other meat for a change. There was no mistaking the gingery-haired clean-cut man in the white jacket, blue and white apron and in summer, the white boater — always obliging, business-like and no waster of words. His successor was a very different man, bold of eye and florid, who was quickly designated a ladies' man from his chaff with the several housewives who were known for giving as good as they got. He came in a flashy open car on order days and it was not long before a forward wife accepted a mid-day ride, while her husband was away in the field earning the family bread. The news of this flew round like wild-fire, while the 'brazen hussy', high on her dignity, declared there was nothing in it, to win the neighbourly response, 'Well, my fine lady, wait till you've had one or two more rides and then we shall see.'

Up-the-Village the general store was constantly busy, handy and ever-obliging in the hands of sister and brother Emily and Johnny Webb, but for household commodities in bulk, valued especially by people living back in the fields, the monthly service of Ebenezer Alfred Illing, Justice of the Peace, Wholesale and Retail Grocer, also of Winslow, was widely used. 'Ebby' ranged far, even as far as Bucknell Lodge Farm, all of fourteen miles from Claydon and near Bicester, where dwelt Gramp and Granny Wright. How delighted and excited was one of the Weir yard boys to be there once for a monthly delivery of large packages of sugar, bags of flour and rice, currants, raisins, tea, cocoa and the like and to have one of Ebby's large sons break open a packet of candied-peel to present him with a glorious, crunchy, tooth-aching lump, because, said jolly 'Twist', he could see the looks of the boy's mother in him while his grandmother and two hovering aunts laughed at his struggles to subdue it, saying they could see the likeness too.

His very being may have resulted from the monthly business and friendly conversations there, because Sally, that mother, when in her 'teens, had gone as nursery-help to Winslow, to Mrs Illing and a large family of young Illings. It was there when she was of sensible age, as George her husband in after years smilingly put it, that Sally looked him over pretty thoroughly and decided that no other would do. She retained a lasting affection for Mrs Illing, visited her often in early years and then looked forward to the visits of 'Twist', or another grown-up son, for monthly business and the two-way exchange of family news, when again it was the Yard's turn for a call.

The larder benefited in a much smaller way from the weekly visits of Arthur Stevens. He dealt mainly in coal and hard-wood deliveries but he often gave a Friday evening call through an open kitchen-door of, 'There's a rabbit hanging up on Jack's hook by the door Mrs Norman — a bob, same as usual. Any time will do', a wild rabbit for the stew-jar which simmered gently in the range. People readily sustained his small side-line. His rabbits were 'got straight-forward', with permission, unlike those of Charlie Jenkins, who needed all his astuteness to avoid the Petty Sessions because of his illicitly got rabbits and the 'Frenchmen', or pheasants with the gorgeous plumage he took in Claydon Woods. Arthur's tall, spare, figure, fresh appearance, ready smile, his instant readiness to help in family extremities, made him twice the man in the view of every mother, fearful lest Charlie's clever wiles, wicked smile and ingenuities in avoiding steady work would ensnare her young as easily as he snared conies. One telling contrast with Arthur was that Charlie's black jowls were shaved only once a week, if that. The Sportsman at Steeple

Claydon was more or less his home. There he was certain of free beer from his capacity to spell-bind the company with outrageous yarns and jokes 'enough to make a cat laugh'. Mothers' faces went grim at any mention of him. He died full of years having lived almost entirely at other people's expense to win for himself a column in the Advertiser — 'Well-known Claydon character dies' — longer than any gained by genuine worthies of the time.

Panter the draper, was a house-to-house caller who owned a shop on the market square in Winslow from which he travelled with dress-materials, ready-made clothing, swatches for the selection of suitings, cottons, linens, silk for linings and the backing of waistcoats. His brown-paper packages carried from his box-cart and placed on a parlour table were a fascination to inquisitive children as with swift skill he opened them to lay out their contents. Bargaining done his dexterity in re-packaging them was a second wonder. Men such as he ran 'clubs' into which village folk paid regular small sums towards larger purchases in times ahead — 'when our Edie gets wed', or 'because my Jack's got it into his head to go to Canada where his friend is and doing well at the lumber-work', or 'my boy's growing out of his clothes that fast it's a job to keep him covered', or 'the girls' pinners wear out before you can look round,' or 'just to have something in hand'. 'Very wise indeed Mrs Timms very wise. See you again a fortnight today' and the dapper man with the smoothed down hair and neat moustache, displaying in person a good serviceable suiting, would be heard within minutes next-door.

Callers were not invariably welcomed. One persistent worrier was Waddesdon John. His smartly turned-out van carried packaged goods, culinary and household, which must have been acceptable around the villages, but he sold little in the Yard. Fortnightly without fail, his ragman-roll at the back doors there ran exactly the same, punctuated at a distance by, 'Not today, Mr Saunders'. He would end, ever in hope, with his, 'Any Mazawattee Tea?' and the inner room voice would reply, firmer than ever, *'Nothing today,* thank you, Mr Saunders'. His airs were in question; his brushed whiskers and eye-brows, his impeccable high collar and cravat and the angled bowler were those of a strutting man of commanding, rather than persuasive, voice who bore himself like a shop-walker in a grand emporium. His opening of the house doors to call his wares was too forthcoming. Perhaps the people at far-off Waddesdon knew no better. If custom he wanted he should not behave as if he owned the village. It was a nicety beyond him, but he persisted and so fell somehow into the village pattern. As in stately style he drove Up-the-Village cheeky boys called, 'Any Mazzywatee Tea? Any monkey-soap?', safely distant.

Another caller who found headway difficult was Fatty Forbes. No other forename was ever bestowed on him in Claydon. He and a brother owned a furniture business in Winslow, their wide shop-front opened on the market-square. Their soft upholstery materials were said, not quite justly perhaps, to be designed to gain entry into homes where antique furniture and old-time bric-à-brac might be discovered and bargained for; where there were pieces in daily use, or set aside, which were of value but to which some owners gave little thought, except that they had been handed down through generations. Tapestries, draught-curtains, bed-spreads, valances and chintzes, were the specialities he carried, so he did not obtrude on Panter's rounds. With these he made entry. Smooth tongued and persuasive in manner he paid many visits and compliments before mentioning that a late eighteenth century cupboard was quite an interesting piece, proceeding then to, 'Mrs Dinton, I wonder whether you and your husband would let me take it off your hands. You could be surprised at what I would give you for it.' 'Any price Fatty offers,' husbands said, 'multiply by ten and then have nothing to do with him'. Occasionally he returned to his brother guardedly elated — a hard-pressed family had at last yielded on the Regency side-table for which he had paid them five golden sovereigns.

It was grievous to see old Mrs Bell's Mother Hubbard corner cupboard carried away. Just as in the nursery rhyme she had often waddled to it to find a boy not a bone but pear-drops in return for small errands done. A comfortable quaintness was suddenly lost.

'I never cease to admire your gate-legged table, Mrs

Hamp,' Fatty said, his plump hands resting in the roll of curtain-material lying on her centre table, 'it's an old piece, you know, taking up space, and the candle-snuffers not much in use nowadays, I suppose?'. 'Open out the roll,' she countered, 'so that I may see the pattern. As for the table and the snuffers, they stay in the family.' The roll was then laid out with a small sigh. When once more he had departed she said to her husband, 'We knew him years ago in Winslow — a well-fed little silky-tongued talker even then'. 'How came you to know about the silky talk Martha?' 'Not the way you think,' she answered. 'He tried it all round just the way he does now.'

Every week the corn-chandler brought barley-meal for cottagers' pigs, oats for horses, mixed corn for back-yard poultry, bran for pet rabbits and millet for cage-birds. A round-faced joking man who never hurried, he had time to gather and dispense items of local news. He was reliable too, in putting right gossip which had gone a little astray. 'Well, if you want to know the facts — it is Jabez Wells of Mursley, you're asking about — nothing to do with Molly Wells here. He's called to court for pinching his boss's eggs and putting 'em with his own for the higgler. Who found him out? He used to go home the back way when his work was done with farm eggs in the side-pockets of his working jacket and one evening the boss noticed how careful Jabe was in climbing the rickyard gate to go home. Curtis gave him the sack on the spot and said he would hear more of it. No — not called for breaking and entering, that's all wrong. It's just the little matter of the eggs. Jabez don't care a damn, you know, got another job straight away. The higgler? He's not in any trouble. How could he know? 'Taint easy to tell one hen's egg from another, now is it? It'll be in the Advertiser. Fined five shillings, I reckon. Thanks very much for the cup of tea, ma'am. Same as usual next week?'

The higgler travelled by pony and trap, carrying large baskets, visiting mostly monthly in the laying season, buying surplus eggs from the farms and the cottagers who owned chicken-runs. The Chapmans had their own run and Hubert owned the daintiest Blue Andalusian you ever saw. She laid her first egg on September the Fifth 1912, Oliver Cromwell's birthday, as Hubert pointed out, showing off a little. Only in the spring flush though did cottagers have spare eggs for this brisk man, Harry Bates from Oving. His remunerative trade was with farmers' wives. More than any dealer he was averse to the intrusive motor-car.

Billy Norton came once a week with shop fruit and vegetables. These, not grown in cottage-gardens, came, like the bakers' wares from nearby Granborough. A frail man, somewhat lame, his open van, drawn by a shaggy brown pony which knew every point of call, Billy was admired through the villages for his spirit and cheeriness and quick readiness to oblige, so people bought readily, if on a small scale, comparing him volubly with one or two locals pronounced too idle to do a hand's turn for themselves, leave alone anybody else. He was important to all children because of the banana, ripe apricot, or William pear, bestowed on the ready boy or girl who, sorry for his limp, carried a delivery for him down a long house-path. Also he brought the orange to go in the Christmas stocking, then a once a year fruit, truth to tell never quite at its sweetest by Christmas Eve, but fitting beautifully in the toe.

An unfailing Monday caller was another Billy — William Madkins of Padbury — in a light cart drawn by a brisk pony. He carried, amongst other small goods the special striped, aniseed-tasting, boiled sweets, famed locally as 'Billy Madkinses', likened by boys to bull's-eyes, only different.

There were other visitors, occasional only, who made a diversion by simply appearing, bringing benefits never to be counted upon. The ringing of a hand-bell would proclaim the presence of a muffin-man in a white apron pacing carefully erect down the village street, a pad on his flat cap, on the pad a tray covered by a clean white cloth. His muffins, though declared somewhat leathery, sold as out-of-the-way tea-time treats. His origins were vague and the source of his muffins vague too — he was a stranger unlikely ever to be a rich man, his wares and custom were meagre, his replenishments where?

A knife and scissors man trundled his treadle-machine through the village about once a year, spinning his carborundum wheel to all-round benefit. Its edging cry brought out custom as he blithely whistled, eyed, felt and ground scissors, knives, edged tools to a frightening sharpness. 'Oh dear — let me have it, ma'am. You could ride bare-back to

Dublin on this one. A blunt knife is more dangerous than a sharp one used right. You'll feel the difference when I've put it to the wheel' and he would treadle hard, sliding the blade to and fro raising sparks and a whine to set teeth on edge. 'Sixpence, if you please, ma'am. See if your man can't shave with it as well as carve the joint a-Sunday!' From his ready words he might have been an Irishman. He changed little from year to year, was well-shaven himself and of a merry eye, wearing always the same bowler and good-quality black coat, both a little green from age and weather. He returned along the lane to the village, whistling notes which had something of *The Lily of Laguna* about them, knowing that Claydon would occupy him until dusk.

There could be the surprise of an enterprising fresh-fish salesman, who, in a basket fixed to the handle-bars of his bicycle, carried a great sad-looking cod from which he would sell cutlets by measure, a rare opportunity indeed. Claydon people were as far from the sea as any in England so the diminishing fish looked lost and was itself a wonder. Some mothers declined to buy, though the man looked professional enough in his straw-hat and striped apron. They thought it more safe to depend on Johnny Webb's bloaters, properly smoked and boxed and collected by him from the railway station on Fridays.

Calling 'Soo-eep, soo-eep!', also around once a year in spring or summer, came 'Poony', the sweep. His calling was from the street — folk went out to him. Regularity was unknown to Poony. The black little man, black sacks, black brushes, black trap, black pony even, just appeared. 'If you need Poony to push his brushes through you'd better go and book him now — he's at Ben White's' and he would not be at Ben White's for certain. When he was found children stood by his tethered pony to watch for his brush to emerge from a chimney-pot, because he always gave it a triumphant twirl when it met day-light. Knowing gardeners waylaid him to beg or buy soot to be stored and grow old for onion-beds, for fat firm bulbs, and for sweet-pea rows, for colour.

In direst worry alarmed children one mid-day saw him lying at the road-side, the pony nudging his still form, blood trickling from his sooty brow, village people gathering in haste and Will Foster, with pail of water, crying, 'Stand back, all. This'll bring him round. He ent cut serious. That bottle was empty before he fell on it. That's the trouble today. No more soo-eeping this day, Poony, my lad.' The threat of water was enough and Poony sat up when Will said sharply, 'Now you children, off to school with you. Can't you hear the bell? You'll be late.' Was Poony drunk, they wondered? They worried, hurrying to afternoon school, for he was an attractive little man when officiating — did disappearing and re-appearing tricks with the six-penny piece he had earned, teeth and eyes shining through his eternal sootiness. Seen only once in a whole year, coming from afar, Poony made himself vividly memorable.

Sometimes a tramp, a vagrant, a travelling-man, made his way to the Yard begging 'a pinch of tea, missis, to go along with this mossul o'sugar your neighbour's just spared me'. The receptacle pushed forward was a cocoa-tin with an improvised wire handle. His detour from the work-house in the High Street in Winslow had to be a wide one getting him to Bicester and a bed there by night-fall. All children eyed such as he from a distance and shuddered when someone recited, 'Hark, hark, the dogs do bark, the beggars are coming to town, some in rags, some in tags and some in silken gowns.' They were alarmingly variable in attire and manner, never one, though, in a silken gown — for which small watchers were thankful — the thought of the silken ones frightened the Weir children thoroughly, for the Bernwood dogs roused easily.

A gipsy woman, wrinkled and walnut-brown, would smile and flatter a housewife into buying clothes-pegs — 'made by the gipsies, ma'am — a hard life, ma'am. Is this your boy? He's going to be a wonder in the world, anybody can see that. Yes, a shilling for the pegs and God bless you for it.' The man of the house later examining the pegs, said, 'All made from green hazel cut from the hedges. The gipsies know they will fall to pieces when they dry — good for custom.' 'Never mind,' his busy wife would respond, 'it's not a life we would choose for ourselves.' A boy destined to be a wonder of some kind once asked a be-shawled old lady, 'How is it that the gipsies know if you are lucky or not? And how do they know better than the people who really know us?'

'What a clever boy you've got here, ma'am!' she said, laughing and patting his shrinking hand with her wrinkled paw. 'That's easy told. You see, gipsies is born under hedges and that means they can see under and through. Only sixpence to get you more true luck, my dears' and his mother laughed too and then bought the lucky charm, a piece of scented wood.

In spring or summer there would be the sudden, explosive, opening notes of a barrel-organ — the one-legged man with the small one-legged organ and the shivering little monkey in a red jacket sitting on his shoulder, or the full-scale organ pushed along like a barrow, the one with a much greater repertoire and far more power. Either drew children to them like magnets. The small takings were pennies drawn from wives' shopping purses, or a passing man's thong-tied moneybag.

An acrobat padding into the village in running-shoes, bowling a carriage-wheel down the street in the way boys trundled iron hoops, was once, and only once, a sensation. That day he drew silver to his collection. He soon had an audience. He needed only to steady his wheel, mount it and run it round the Cross Tree for the news of him to spread, children the front-runners. A tiny wizened old man, lithe as a cat in a singlet and shorts, no hat, his belongings in a canvas bag which he placed on the Cross Tree seat, he turned somersaults back and forth, walked on his hands, stood on his wheel to twirl it with his toes till its spokes turned to mist, shouting, 'Easy does it! Easy does it! Who's for having a go?' His *pièce de resistance* no-one would consider imitating for a second — the throwing of a large garden potato vertically high in the air, standing under it to allow it to fall plumb on his waiting fore-head, where it shattered to fragments.

'My God, old chap,' Jimmy Janes cried, 'what a way to get a living! Here, take this bob to get you something to eat' and Jimmy was not known to be free with his money. Others felt for six-penny and three-penny pieces, suddenly shamefaced and worried. As he went bowling away Up-the-Village adults and children alike though amazed and amused at what they had seen, worried that a man who might well be a grandfather should do this. 'A circus man who's lost his job', someone guessed. Such visitors fell into no pattern, brought passing interest, sometimes such chastening thoughts as these, and were never certain to come down to the Weir, for which all there felt thankful.

Then there was the inevitable rag-and-bone man, quite irregular, who, strangely, seemed never to collect bones. Regarded as an oddity he was strikingly dressed for the part, in particular in an old silk hat. His bundles, festooned on a rickety cart drawn by a shambling horse, contained old clothes and materials bought for next-to-nothing and destined for great mysteries. Rabbit skins were exchanged for trifles like paper windmills on sticks, paper flowers and sometimes a gold-fish to go in your jam-jar of water. Sometimes it was hard to decide from voice or attire whether, or not, the rag-and-bone man was in fact male.

A stranger, more orthodox, could arrive with a shop-on-wheels hung outside with turnery, showing inside shelves of it with culinary utensils in variety, which folk gathered to examine under the watchful eye of the vendor who clashed sauce-pans together to speed the slow-comers. Pronounced a one-day wonder he was handy, nevertheless, to newly — and to-be-weds. 'A frying-pan for your bottom drawer, Maisie?' a saucy bystander would say, while older wives whose pans and boilers had grown thin from decades of firing, examined long before they bought.

Such occasional callers were not door-to-door men; folk had to go out to them, as also to the cheap-jack who laid out his array of china beneath the Cross Tree for Dutch auction.

From time to time evangelising people settled in a road-side field for as long as a week, their van proclaiming in beautiful sign-writing Biblical warning, exhortation and provisional promise. They certainly were callers, and to every single door, with leaflets, booklets and invitations to their evening services in the gospel tent, urging that ways of life should be re-considered and drastically and without delay, altered. 'What' children enquired worriedly at home, 'is the Wrath to Come?' There was awful sudden concern about Judgment Day and talk of the end of the world, for the wrath seemed to be immediately consequent on the co-incidence of both. The younger sorts felt guilty relief when at last the camp-ground was at peace again, trampled but its old self. They were assured only a little by the answers given.

Comfortably and in fairly orderly fashion the ordinary house-to-house callers helped to maintain the Yard's own sort of regularity. It resembled the ticking of the alarum-clock in a back-bedroom there, which co-operated best by lying on its face, refusing to act as was expected — very much like some amongst the village people — and seeming to smile as they did at secret knowledge.

So — Tommy Heritage with fresh bread on Tuesdays and Fridays, always at about the same time of day; Colgrove, or the flamboyant man, on Wednesdays and Saturdays about chump-chops, stewing beef, Sunday joints; each Thursday Billy Norton, should you fancy a cucumber, Conference pears, or require Seville oranges for marmalade; Monday Arthur Stevens with coal and enquiring about logs, but on Friday evening with a rabbit; on Wednesday morning the pottle of mixed corn left in the out-house by Ernie Bedford, should the trusting house-wife be abroad. Then, fortnightly, Panter's drapery, Waddesdon John's patter, and monthly Ebby Illing, or one of his sons; Fatty Forbes and, in season, the higgler, with the cheerful hail of Louie, the post-lady, a most admirable regulator. All helped the communal clock to tick away through the village in services taken for granted, disturbed only by the untoward — such as the higgler's pony's mistaking the flash of turnery and clashing of sauce-pans for a dreaded motor-monster, or Jim Parkin's wife's acceptance of the motor-ride observed by half the village, a venture she dare not repeat, or the draper's cob's loose shoe and delay at the forge. And the occasional visitors provided interesting hiccups, as did the alarum clock when it threatened to stop but invariably revived to pound along more resolutely than ever.

The Yard children were unfailingly alive to all these comings and goings, if not always comprehending them. They felt the callers to be making a pattern of their days, changing at times, loosely woven into the texture of life as it must be lived; but livened by the occasional startling moment, as once on 'Mr Panter's day', the alternate Tuesday when he had new towelling laid out on the Chapmans' front-room table, their mother, indecisive about it, she exclaimed, 'Questions! everlasting questions! Go and steady Mr Panter's horse, boy, while Tom Giles passes with the reaper. Take these sugar-lumps for the pony' and then, as the boy left, 'How would you explain to a boy what a *bold bissom* is, Mr Panter?'

THE CLUB FEAST

Once again the late summer weather favoured the first Saturday in September, the day of the festival. The mid-morning sun from a blue sky shone on a growing crowd gathering outside the village-hall. Others had been busy inside it almost from first light. The Sick Benefit Club's annual feast, time-honoured, must be celebrated properly right through the day. First there would be the parade to church for a service at eleven o'clock. Most members and many others were already gathering for this. The club's banner would lead the brass-band and the procession of members there and with them, all who cared to join them in sober Sunday fashion. Thus there was some pushing forward, with chatter, smiles and cheers, when two members emerged from the hall carrying the banner, which had lain there, rolled up in its box, waiting a whole year for its day to come round again.

The men unrolled it, raising it high by its poles for the breeze to take it, to reveal its silk fresh as paint, its central motif a spreading tree in full leaf and at the top *Manchester Unity Friendly Society Sir Harry Verney Lodge of Oddfellows* in ornate gold lettering in a scroll and at the bottom, if only the breeze would allow you to read them, the words *Brothers in Need*. It embodied in rippling sheen all that the sick club stood for. Chosen members only must bear it and lead the way.

Slipper Price, who invariably bore the storm-lantern for the band's winter excursions, steadied one pole and another unmusical member held the other. It was Slipper's great day. He wore his best and only suit, rarely seen since he was wedded to his Lizzie at the time of Queen Victoria's golden jubilee. He looked a little shrunken in it but he stood ram-rod straight, gripping his pole, for the wind worked determinedly on the banner, while keeping his eye on Jackie the band-leader, who would give direction. The bandsmen, all the club-members and the other men joining them likewise wore their Sunday-best suits, dark and well-pressed, few of modern cut, and were wearing also the hard black hats with curled brims seen usually only at funerals. These on the whole were not happily angled, but there was perfection in the polish of the black boots. Weathered features and hands looked strange against such a mass of Sunday-go-to-Meeting attire. Here and there a wife hurried to them to set a high white collar straight, or to adjust a trouser-leg over a boot-top, or to flick a speck of dust from a broad shoulder. To laughter and cheers she would retire flushed, not wanting to be thought fussy.

The bandsmen, now formed in couples, looked so impressive that the watchers gave them a full cheer, Hubert glowing with pride from having father and grandfather amongst them and Sid, because his uncle bore the drum. The moment had come for Jackie to get them away, but first, having doubts about Slipper's obvious excitement, he paced out the distance to be kept between banner and band for the march. That done and smiling knowingly to the crowd, he placed himself at the front of his men and raised his cornet to announce, 'We'll blow proud every step o'the way, men, and Jimmy, we shall want to hear the drum firm and clear to keep us going right to the church. I shall count to four. Are we ready then?' He blew down his cornet for a clear passage, his round face beamed, his brown eyes shone, he drew breath, counted to four at the pace he wanted and *The Soldiers of the Queen* burst forth with command and vigour exactly right. The watchers raised their cheers to three, dogs barked, the children prepared to follow and the breeze took a powerful hold on the banner as it led into the road and then into Church Walk the long procession. There they progressed through sunshine and green shade beneath the over-hanging hornbeams, where the first notes of the church-bell were heard beckoning them on into the path through Church Spinney. There their sounds fell away and there their young followers deserted them to rush back in a skelter to the hall. Distantly on went the band, diminishing all the time in sound but for the steady throb of the drum, until, after ten minutes or so there came silence. They had arrived. The rector stood at St Mary's gate to receive them, saying quietly to himself, 'Gracious — what a concourse!' His sidesmen hovered at the porch against what he had termed eventualities — 'More folks than ever, Albert,' one commented. The company seemed to stretch far beyond their vision. The rector turned to give them a signal and then turned to his congregation to lead them in, steadying his pince-nez, for the breeze was stiff, the banner plainly troublesome.

Early in the morning Johnny Webb of the General Store had harnessed his mare to take the flat-bed trolley to Claydon House to collect the trestle-tables and laundry lent for the feast. He had to be early for the mare was slow and the load heavy, so it had been, 'Come alongee, come along-ee!' all the way on an errand so serious that the running boys who joined him in the village forgot for once to join him in chorus, but ran ahead to warn the hall people that Johnny was coming and to be ready to be enlisted for help. Thus, long before St Mary's bell began its call Sergeant Daniels, the caretaker, Johnny and their helpers were erecting the tables in precise lines the length of the hall-floor. That done, the women took from the laundry-baskets white table-cloths beautifully ironed and folded — all packed by Mrs Hall herself. She, in charge of the House-laundry, was renowned for her folding and whitenesses. When all the tables were covered that renown was proclaimed again and acclaimed almost in awe. Her covers lay like a fall of undinted snow.

Meanwhile to clapping and loud cheers outside, pony-traps drew up, one from Bernwood Farm, then Percival from Claydon House, then Tompkins of East Claydon, on his lap a large case containing knives known to be of frightening efficiency for he was a butcher who was also a farmer. Unloading began at once of heavy meat-dishes, white cloths covering a baron of beef, sirloins and steaks, shoulders and legs of lamb and mutton and assorted joints of pork all roasted in distant ovens and brought cold. Tompkins was joined within minutes by two fellow farmers hurrying in, first Lester of Bernwood, carrying an impressive case of carvers with heavy brass clasps and then small peppery McNab, the Scotsman who had introduced horned mountain-sheep to Claydon and so a mutton of special sweetness, carrying his case of carvers quite reverently. At the side-tables in the hall they set about giving an expert display of blade-sharpening on steels, testing with their thumbs edges keen as razors; next each cut a first delicate slice, inspected it closely and, pronouncing it perfect, bestowed broad smiles all round and flourished their knives in playful fashion as the women brought them piles of plates for their work. The baron of beef was assigned to Tompkins, now in blue and white apron and straw hat. All three sliced away with equal enviable skills, working their way methodically to the sweetness next to bone after bone, the women marvelling at their work and bearing it away plate after plate, the men the while commenting with knowledge and arguing a little on such matters as choice of cut, hanging for ripeness, roasting, when to baste, garnishing and, very occasionally, the age of a sliver raised on the prongs of a fork, vowing that all before them would go the same way home and by two o'clock at the latest.

It was a splendid moment. Three Claydon men of substance stood carving away, filling plate after plate and perspiring a little, while the club-members' wives moved to and fro with plates, crockery and cutlery to have all ready for the men at twelve-thirty. Children crowded the doorways anxious for assurance by their mothers that hot fruit puddings would also be brought in proper time. All this while the men, almost all of whom had laboured for these and other farmers throughout the year, sat before the rector in church in their best clothes, some a little cramped, all circumspect, knowing that their banner and the band would lead them to a fine meat-tea, during which they would be waited upon like gentry.

The farmers knew well enough what the banner symbolised, that the Sick Benefit Club was a vitally necessary stand-by for the men and their families. All on field-work were members, as were those engaged at the brick-works and the fewer railway-men. Subscriptions of a few pence each week, collected monthly by the honorary secretary, who circulated the villages on his bicycle, ensured modest maintenance should they fall ill or sustain injury at work, when the weekly wage usually failed at once. Parish Relief and the work-house in Winslow were to be avoided at all costs. The club-money was regularly put aside in all households, along with a strong general wish never to call upon the club for help. Men boasted that they had 'paid in the club for years without ever drawing a penny' and they spoke wryly, often unsympathetically, of one who frequently had aid, naming him 'a proper casualty man', even though the club's doctor took him off work.

Also, there was the further powerful incentive of the annual feast to keep the funds strong. Each August, according to the rules, the treasurer presented the accounts when again according to custom a large part of the balance-in-hand went to providing the feast. The local gentry often gave money to help as did better-off farmers and their wives, while others gave over their ovens for roasting the meats and their coppers for boiling the fruit-puddings.

It was a good hour before the carving men could remove their aprons and re-encase their tools. Surveying the preparations they decided that, once again, they were up to standard and perhaps a little beyond — the organisation under Daniels was the better for having a military air about it. Amidst many thanks, rich laughter and jokes some time-worn, they left. They had made their contribution. They would leave all now, they said, to the men's enjoyment. It was the men's day. Leave them to it.

Hubert, Harry and Sid in the fore-front of a press of children in the doorway, gazed in wonder at the transformation of the hall where week by week, for Sunday school they sat in their Bible-reading circles — changed utterly. Potted plants now fronted the stage and at intervals on the long tables, amidst the rows of place-settings, stood vases of late summer flowers, sweet peas, golden marigolds and early chrysanthemums. Often had their easily lost attention wandered to the hall's interior arrangements, solemnly to the large framed photographs of the two young men in officers' uniforms and wide hats, farmers' sons, who had died far from home in the Boer War and to that picture on the end wall of the sad lady in a white dress bending over a harp and playing on just one string, all the others being broken. More often their thoughts dwelt on the long narrow box lying high on a side-shelf, its lid today left raised, in which lay the club banner waiting and waiting for the next Feast Day. One day, when quite grown-up, they might have the honour of bearing it to church where now it was that very day. Firmly they stuck to their posts in the doorway in order to miss nothing in the hall, while at the same time holding themselves ready to run to meet the banner on its return.

Meanwhile the banner stood displayed in St Mary', spread against the chancel-wall, coloured lights from stained glass patterned on it, the bandsmen sitting in chairs below it resting their instruments, the rows of pews full to overflowing.

The rector had led the way for the long settling-in. It gave him time to refresh the words he had prepared. They would point powerfully to the significance of this annual occasion, the hymns should comfort and assure, the theme *Art thou poor yet hast thou golden slumbers, O sweet content* — and, of course, for a hymn, *Work for the night is coming.* Solemnly he looked down upon his congregation, a number vastly swollen and, sitting extremely awkwardly he thought, many of other persuasions and others whose faces he could not place, looking slowly round at the unfamiliar vaulting, arches and stained glass.

But to begin, because clearly there was a general desire that he should, so he stood tall and began and patiently was he followed. He was ever prone to preach at a level somewhat above village comprehension and he saw no reason to simplify today, so he did not. He elaborated considerably on frugality and foresight and twice he thumped the lectern on a point. However, although he detected no restlessness, just a distant staring by some of the unknowns into the higher distances of the vaulting, he saw that he must not keep them long. Within forty minutes, with the help of a harvest hymn and *Work for the night is coming,* his sidesmen could move into the aisles as all stood for the band to play a verse of the *Old Hundredth,* when, right on, was played and sung *All People that on Earth do well,* all the verses with admirable vigour, even gusto here and there, while the rector, still singing, descended to place himself at the church-door. With the organ sustaining the final chord magnificently his congregation moved out as he stood smiling and shaking hands with each one, thus getting a close view of everyone. His church at last emptied fell again into its customary Saturday morning stillness and he, with the sidesmen, stepped outside to see the procession re-form in the confines of gravelled path, encroaching yews and aged, leaning tombstones at the verge; but, with conversation now possible and all tension eased, it was managed, while several members murmured together, 'He didn't keep us long — it passed over very well again,' but another, a little loudly, 'He was above me all through. What's the time?' On him, a man neither church nor chapel, as one might expect, but a good club man all the same, the rector cast a long look compounded of a faint frown and a swift smile. He stood again at the gate to see them go. Jackie, his men and the banner were already in position at the fore-front, Jackie poised for a smart return progress. The band had no extensive repertoire, but they had a resourceful leader. He had adapted their favourite polka to become a jigging march, so that when they moved off they picked up their heels surprisingly, setting their banner into some jaunty stepping in order to keep ahead, the rector watching them until the last of the walkers disappeared into Church Spinney. Children in large numbers lay in wait to march beside the band, Hubert, Sid and Harry in the van, all the way back to the hall where the arrival was something of a triumph.

Slipper and his companion carried the banner in to the sergeant, who had it positioned high on the stage, where it would overlook the feast and where for a brief rest, they sat below it, arms folded, viewing the loaded tables stretched before them with happy and completely undisguised satisfaction. But it was twelve-thirty and the sergeant now in the doorway was calling in sergeant-majorly tones, 'Attention all! Members forward now. You will be seated by name, so ears sharp, eh?' The seating was organised, some thought over-organised, by this commanding man, but none demurred. The club secretary and treasurer on his either side, he began with, 'Brother Atkins - J' and ended with, 'Brother Wilde - E., of Verney Junction, I think,' folding his list to hand it to the Secretary, while Ernie Wilde, last to enter and last to sit, said loudly, 'Alphabetical again — I knew how it'ud be wi' the likes o' me,' looking round to wave to a distant sitter, 'old pals together for once 'ud ha' bin nice, but there — this is the sergeant's realm, best to humour him. We're here for business, anyway.' On that the buzz of conversation hushed. The rector, a little breathless after a change of garments and hurrying beyond his usual gait, had arrived to say grace. All rose for his *May the Lord bless what His bounty hath provided*, after which, to a great noise of scraping chair-legs, all sat. The Rector saying yes, he would take a little and what a gathering yet again it was, sank to his reserved place at the officials' table — but the real business had already begun.

A meat-tea was an infrequent joy. There might well be no other for a complete year. Application to it was serious. Quality and quantity were appraised, approved, praised and despatched with deliberation in which speed played no part. Dickens's white bread, new from his bake-house at Granborough, various pickles, salt and mustard were the accompaniments. Steady going was all that was required for thirty-minutes and more, with second, even third, helpings smilingly available, when hot fruit puddings would crown the feast. Cheers outside announced their arrival by pony-trap from the kitchens of their several provenances. They were carried steaming to the side-tables where members' wives began swiftly to uncover and apportion them. This was a tense moment for Hubert and the other children crowding the doorway. Were they cloth-puddings, the kind which had wrinkled ends from the tying? — ends laid aside as unsuitable presentations to the men? Last year such worthwhile morsels had been the reward of willing young helpers after the meal's end in the clearing-up. Assurance was whispered round — Sid's mother had signalled to him — yes, cloth-puddings again. All jostling ceased, decorum prevailed, smiles and nods. Ample portions laid before them the members again paid tribute to the labours, the high professionalism of the distant cooks and, as they progressed with their duff, some claimed to deduce its precise origin from the nature, placing, distancing of the fruit and peel within it — not by way of criticism, far from that, just a mention as a matter of interest and yes, please, another slice.

Quite soon it was all over, but for the president's and the officials' thanks to the organisers and helpers and the rector's closing words, which spoke once more of the rewards of toil, both for body and spirit, of the plain sense of everyday good management, from which rewards such as today's came, of the wisdom, which members displayed throughout each year, of always having in mind the rainy day and even on such a joyous late summer's day as this still bearing it in mind — a blessing then and then a long, slow withdrawal into the open air with the time almost at two o'clock.

The solemnities were over, a feast to remember through another year, but more was to be done on the day which had its immovable place in the local calendar, held in esteem above all others, above the national rest days, above even the occasional grand local celebrations. Edward the Seventh's Coronation had brought one and some years later had come another that of his son George the Fifth. There were the Liberal Demonstrations on the Claydon House lawns and the jollity there at the christening of an heir — pleasant indeed were all of these for dressing-up and meeting folk in large numbers, for renewing acquaintanceships, for happy exchanges, joining in sports, fun and sit-down teas. But they were fortuitous gatherings. The Club Feast was different. Tied up with men's comradeship at work and in their few hours of leisure, with seriousness about health and family maintenance — always, somewhere, only just in balance — when achieved yet again it was a return for prudence and steadfastness. Furthermore it was their very own.

The afternoon sun promised to shine on warmly as it had begun, first on the tug-of-war competition, a grave affair, unfailingly diverting. Teams of eight of the weightiest, most muscled, hard-boned men would pull preliminary pulls towards a final. The grass verge outside the hall was the venue and the sergeant — and none more physical than he — the arranger and the referee. It was as time-honoured as the feast. The crowd pressed heavily forward, but gave space for desperate heaving, grunting and slithering, from which the men of Botolph Claydon and of Verney Junction emerged as finalists. This was a surprise. Never before had the railwaymen reached this eminence. True, they were shod to a man in hob-nailed boots, having exchanged their Sunday boots for them immediately the feast was over, their wives quietly conniving. But their opponents felt no alarm. They had themselves pulled Middle Claydon over with ease and had then seen that East Claydon would have done the same with the hob-nailed men, had their front man but kept his feet — he had suddenly sat down. Verney Junction? — shunters, plate-layers, a signal-man and a ticket-collector? — pretenders.

The onlookers pushed close forward and the two teams took up their lengths of the rope. 'Go on, Botolph — show 'em!' went up a great cry, 'you've got three Becketts — pull 'em into Kingdom Come!', as a railway supporter quietly urged, 'Don't let 'em snatch you sudden — hold like one man — then snatch *them*.' Snatch is what Botolph set out to do at once and with a first gigantic heave it appeared they had done it, but the white tape on the rope stopped and hovered directly above the ground-mark, hovered and then stayed motionless, the sergeant's nose within an inch of it, his eyes watching, both hands raised signalling balance. The railwaymen had their heels grounded as in concrete and were holding — a Botolph man near the back gently swore. Temples and jugular veins swelled and swelled, eyes took on fixed stares, then glazed, muscles set like iron and sixteen men and the rope itself solidified, went rigid as if all were one and still the tape stayed unmoved, the sergeant tense above it, hands exactly as at first, motionless, apparently not breathing, his eyes fixed on the scrap of white tape. This could not last. No man on either side seemed to be breathing. Their faces had turned from red to deep purple and now the watchers grew alarmed. Several wives pushed almost to their men on the rope crying, 'Give up men, it ent worth it' and 'Give up, Frank — oh, my poor man, look at him' and 'Make 'em stop, sergeant, it's stalemate' and 'Give up, Jabez, this minute. Don't you hear me?', but neither Jabez, nor Frank, nor any man in either team showed response.

Minutes passed. Equal opposite weights frightening in stolidity, hung awesomely in an alarmed stillness until, at last, came a movement, a sudden concerted wriggling of iron heels into the turf and, with that, a heave and then a quick, jerking, heave and then another and another, quicker still, almost explosive, and then the tape was seen to move and the men of Botolph *en masse*, to slither, gouging up great turves, staring skywards in sudden desperation as the sergeant raised his hand, when they sat down together with never a word, and the railwaymen rose smiling, fondling the rope. No prize was awarded, nor ever desired. Supreme triumph was enough, with the demonstration that thirty-two men of the parish could take a mighty meal and a mighty contest in one stride with never an apoplexy for any one of them. It was revealed that the victors had practised in the marshalling-yard with rope attached to a loaded freight-wagon. This might happen again, so this club feast saw a change of rule, that all foot-wear in the tugs-of-war should be the same in future. Thus hob-nails became the order of the day.

The children's races following in the adjacent field showed future club-members in competition quite as dedicated and their tea at four-thirty as purposeful as everything so far seen. The social in the evening drew a packed audience to the hall. The singing, dancing, displays at the piano, jolly monologues in this were, as the local news-man expressed it, enjoyed by all, especially the moments when participants persuaded up from the floor demonstrated that they were as rusty as they protested they were. As another club-year closed it ended with the hoary time-honoured finale, *I come from the country my name it is Giles, I've travelled a hundred and forty odd miles*, sung powerfully by the master-of-ceremonies himself, many wry verses on the theme of the countryman's first visit to town, each verse followed by a chorus increasing in delight and power every time round, for, as the MC declared, urging a magnificent crescendo, the words were simple: *Ri-toodle, ri-toodle, ri-toodle, ri-ay!* Enjoyed by all, barring perhaps the rusty hopefuls, were true words.

To the end the club banner stood or hung where the sergeant and its bearers had placed it as a back-cloth to all that transpired on the stage, just as it had adorned the feast. When all was done and the members, their families and friends were tramping homewards under the stars, the members to the lightest of suppers, the pole-bearers helped the sergeant to roll it, to place it in its box, to lift it to the wall-shelf and to close the lid.

That done the sergeant smiled, saying, 'This was your big day, then — your year, so to speak, with the banner. Enjoyed the day, have you?'

'Yes — it's come round,' Slipper said, dreamily.

'Enjoyed?' his mate responded, 'miles more than that, sergeant. This day 'ull stay wi' me the rest of my life.'

But Slipper stood silent for a full half-minute, then said, 'How can a man find the words to say?' — pausing again to look around the now all but empty hall. The sergeant did not press him, still smiled amusedly on both.

'Beautiful,' Slipper said at last, 'that's the word I want.'

MR PURCHASE'S PENNY PICTURES

One memorable autumn afternoon they arrived, the Living Pictures — a penny for children, six-pence for grown-ups. A small steam-engine, floridly painted, drew a van garishly lettered and postered, puff-puffing gently past the school, making for the village-hall close by. The school, with its modern low clear windows, gave a good view of all that passed.

Heads craned. 'Bossie' White, the headmaster, sought out a generous instinct and permitted his charges to stand, to turn, to see. No crunching Council steam-roller passed this time, not the steam thresher and drum of Tommy Alderman, nor the majestic steam ploughs, not R. G. White's fussy little engine hastening mineral waters to Webbs' shop, nor yet the odd horseless carriage. The utmost confines of the great world were creeping in upon the village with sweet and gentle puffs.

'Front, turn! Seats, *One* — seats, *Two*, Sit!' Thus were they regimented. Dimly came Bossie's voice as with chalk he wrote, 'Bios = life, skopein = to look at', for ears were stretched to the limit of other hearing. Had the puffing stopped? Had the Pictures, for the very first time in their lives and at that moment, reached the hall for sure? There seemed to be a silence. Young souls were stolen away in a moment of time. The future was imminent, something important and new was before them — it was down at the village hall, for sure.

The hush of the school-room was complete. Bossie, having had his say about the passing wonder, his bold blue eyes and daunting moustache ensured quiet progress towards four o'clock. He was well aware that application could lapse, attention might wander and certainty about book-learning falter, but all were with him — all wanted four o'clock. When it came the correctness of departure was a pleasure to behold. Sweetly they sang the closing prayer asking for protection and quiet sleep through the darkness of the coming night; quietly were the desk-lids and seats raised precisely on the order, careful were they not to clang their hob-nails on the iron cross-bars of the desks, stepping — 'one — two!' — into the gangways; and how surprising it was to hear Charlie Whitmarsh murmur on leaving, 'Goodnight, Sir' and how surprised Bossie was to hear himself saying, 'Er-er. Goodnight, boy'. He too was confronted by the unusual.

Free, they left him alone with his Bios to rush, push, leap, yell and run headlong helter-skelter to meet Texas, Pearl White, Roscoe Arbuckle, Tom Mix and sit with Romans dressed in altogether peculiar clothes above that awful arena down at the village-hall.

There the van was drawn up, the engine stationary and smoothly digesting, cables already passed from its vitals into the hall's interior, the secrets of the van given by busy men to it with surprising precision and speed. Boys were first at the door, girls right behind, pushing, jumping up and down to see, while the men bustled to and fro liking noise it seemed, whistling, banging, jollying, tolerant — 'so long as you don't get under foot, sonny. Hey up — mind your heads!'

With smiles they were allowed to the threshold, jostling, peeping, wondering, while two or three of the girls by charm and elbow secured places right inside the doorway to be met with, 'Hello, hello, hello, lovely ladies! Make way, *if* you please!' and this with a lordly raising of the hat. The lovely ladies giggled quite ridiculously and moved a step further forward, nudging right and left. These men were different from the village men. They were slim and lively with cheeky looks, quick banter, their hats mostly askew; they had gay kerchiefs round their necks like the fair people, but were not so rough. The boys pulled the girls to draw them back: they had gone quite far enough.

In the hall's depths stood a tall figure stooping over the parish piano. He raised the lid to strike masterly chords and such an astonishing glissando that the modest upright trembled, awakened to things hitherto unimagined. The church organist, it was claimed, could make her talk, but now amidst a cascade of tinklings and bouncing octaves, she sang. He closed her vibrant lid with an air of — well, this-will-do and left. His watchers stared stock-still in wonderment.

Light! — sudden blinding light. Dazzled, they blinked to see the hall's interior transformed, the seating entirely reversed, a huge white sheet on the far wall — waiting. Outside long strings of coloured light sprang to life and flickered promising after-dark brilliance for the hall's front. Electricity, bright and searching, the little engine was making it steadily, mysteriously, gently. Strange shadows thrilled the children. They shrilled, jostled and jigged among them.

But soon the busy men declared it was tea-time — time to go home and tell the folks. For a little some lingered, especially those girls, but then they ran, fled to their teas and breathless tales, tales to draw old heads from chimney-corners, tales to send whole households late to bed, because though Claydon people were ever guarded in statement they knew that something unusual was stirring. The fly-posting had been good. For more than a week with or without permission, tree, wall and post had flamed the words: 'LIVING PICTURES' with added crude, bright and daring illustrations of things beyond rural ken. Surely it was essential to view anything so confidently claimed to be 'KOLOSSAL! ! ! !' It was a bounden duty. Children often heard adult opinion on bounden duty which sorely puzzled them, but there was no ambiguity about this one.

By seven-fifteen the world and his wife had gathered to the hall. Shy men from remote farms and lone places blundered to seats too small for their powerful corduroys; the two leather-faced game-keepers were there and Police-Sergeant Barnes, always alert for eventualities in a new situation, stood talking to the parish constable. Near them, bold as brass and lavish with roguish blind-side winks, stood the two well-known poaching characters, Charlie Jenkins and Boney Beckett, surprisingly smartened, their hats under their arms. Elderly spinsters sat polishing their spectacles, complete families contrived to keep together, the children wriggling, staring and awe-struck, the parents murmuring a little about the brisk man taking the money at the door — he had to be watched regarding the giving of change.

'Must we dress up for this?' one father had grumbled — 'We shall all be in darkness.'

'Not before and not after,' his fussing wife stated firmly and then, certain as Fate,

'And will you ever learn to tie a tie! Bless me, you are as helpless as the children!' and then, as they entered the throng,

'Keep together.'

Village people of all sizes and sorts were gathering,

except for the House Folk who habitually and loftily went to and fro in the wider world; also the ultra-respectable who dwelt on their fringes, those who regularly found mixing altogether trying; also several of the church- and chapel-going kind who saw the Devil's work wherever they looked, having frowned upon the whole incursion from the beginning, deciding now that He was at work in their very midst.

None in the hall gave any of these, including the Unholy One, a single thought. The hungry sheep looked up waiting to be fed. Besides, the Rector was present, standing at the back chatting and smiling. Seeing him, the boys looked carefully over the assembly for the tall figure, blue eyes and moustachios of Bossie, but he was not to be seen. They decided that his grand presence was denied them and felt the better for it.

Brilliant white light, marvellously revealing, shone searchingly upon the assemblage, far beyond the power of the hall's customary oil-lamps' gentle glow. It showed that several of the village's most muscular types, rugged all-weather men, were present, those who never ordinarily removed the hat, indoors or out, summer or winter, but who now did so out of a half-realised reverence for the staring white sheet or for the historic moment, adopting airs of uncommon deference as they sat in a heavy grunting quietude, while grumbling together at the notices which forbade smoking, muttering that a quid of Black Twist would harm nobody.

And here, too, it was observed that by arriving early a whole bevy of lovely ladies of the younger sort had achieved seating as close as possible to the piano. Also stacked three-deep alongside the hall, were the bicycles of the people from afar, some not known at all. Those Police-Sergeant Barnes and Special-Constable Marks quietly eyed. Incomers, recognised or half-known, were quizzed or gently chaffed as they pressed in to settle, apologetic to a man and most careful not to overlap, adding a further strangeness to the occasion.

With five minutes to go the tall young man made rendezvous with the piano. The lighting dimmed and a long bluish-white beam found them. The lovely ladies, caught too, clung together and shivered. All eyes turned and necks craned for a view of this pale gangling figure nonchalant and assured, as he raised the lid, his eyes lazily hooded, a creature not remotely of their world. His rakish felt hat tilted to its farthest backward extremity, his hair long and unkempt, he sat down to a sigh from nearby and with long slim hands at once collected all the keys in a crashing sweep to bring them 'up upon an heap' of arpeggio and chord, to spread them out in double-glissando, following that with bouncing octaves and fairy ripplings beyond belief. The trembling upright fell to this Lothario without a blush — the whole assemblage drew breath as he played serenely on.

Seven-thirty. To a general murmuring and stir the lighting dimmed further, diminished to a mere glow, as away back on the stage behind began the purr of fairy machinery. A long strong beam leapt to the screen, bringing a shifting of seats and limbs and children's excited chatter. One and all sat riveted to the compelling beam, the piano tinkling away, softly rippling in a seductive 'till ready.' The beam then expanded to become a great rectangle in which suddenly huge photography sprang to life, jerky, blurred black and white, so strange that wonder turned to laughter and then to silence when it was seen that dreadful things were afoot — a gang of rough men appeared in a desolate valley of rocks, a beautiful maiden lay cruelly bound by these ruffians across a railway-track, in the distance was the billowing smoke of an approaching train: it was to be the unravelling of *The Exploits of Elaine*.

Romans followed — an amphitheatre seating thousands, charioteers, gladiators, lions, slave-masters, Christians in a blur of crude colour and in such confusion that how all the captured Christians were eventually set free was totally unclear; but it was a breath-stopping business, so unnerving that children pressed close to fathers and mothers for the assurance of their solid presence or drew far back in worried excitement.

It was at that moment that a sturdy stoic shifted position to say loudly, 'Seemingly it's always raining in foreign parts.' Hastily his neighbour muttered,

'It's not rain, man. It's marks on the fillum,' upon which the first man fell silent, while Mrs Perkins, sitting next, gave Mr Perkins a nudge and he said,

'I wondered myself.'

And so it went on with charioteers, cattle-herds, the great lumbering train coming straight at the seated rows to career, stampede and disappear into the dark space overhead, the machinery whirring behind, the pianist in masterful fashion matching it all with sound, from charge right through to fateful dawn, sending the lovely ladies into a dream. Reflected light trembled on them, while he, using no note of a score, a lazy eye on the moving screen, lit cigarette after cigarette with never a pause and well was that noted by the village lads and the men fingering their cold pipes. He rose at the end, standing to play for The King, still chewing the same straw, so to speak, a strange young Lothario whose hooded glance never for a moment abashed those closely pressing daughters of Claydon, who had drawn them as some sort of languid Pied Piper, who rose to leave them with never a word or a nod.

'What did you make of it then?' began one as one and all trailed out into the night. They had been up the Yukon River into saloons where shootings, smashings, philanderings were, as another said, ten a penny, had sat high above that great Roman arena, had seen the trampled sand and the hard faces of gladiators and spectators alike. They had roared as Arbuckle cavorted in a bath only slightly larger than his monstrous self, had seen Pearl White on the edge of calamities likely and unlikely to survive in last seconds of time, had smirked and bridled at the simperings of lovers weirdly white of face and gesticulating to the point of ridicule.

There had been no immediate or direct answer to that question. As yet young and old, family folk, bachelors, spinsters, poachers, police, game-keepers, grumbly old smokers and visitors, were in a daze, startled, baffled, aching around the ribs, unsettled in feelings of daring, having allowed the outside world in in an unguarded hour. The home-going beneath the stars was a bemused traverse through the dark street and lanes in a clamour of bicycle-bells and goodnights and then almost a silence.

*   *   *   *   *   *

In the cold light of the next day Harry Wiggins, Sid Jennings and Billy Price stood with a small mixed crowd to view the departure. The little engine puff-puffed as purposefully away as at its coming, the multi-coloured van again coupled behind and, leaning from it, a figure raised and then waved a hat and soon, but for their smoke, they disappeared amongst the distant hedges and were gone.

'I wonder what Granborough will make of it,' George Norman said, giving the small imperial on his chin thoughtful strokes, 'That's where they're headed — a sleepy lot there. Might liven 'em up a bit.'

'Made a change for us, anyway,' Jimmy Warner added 'out of the usual run, as you might say,' and again as he moved slowly off, 'out of the usual run.'

A change? Those boys knew for absolute certainty that they had witnessed a fantasy — scare-y at times, fascinating, ridiculous, unpredictable, comedy outrageous, no real world at all. Incontrovertible final proof lay in the fact that *all wheels in every conjured up scene* involving chariot, covered wagon, buggy, steam-train, or car, amazingly *revolved backwards* while propelling the vehicles forwards. It was an absurdity which in school Bossie himself quite failed to explain away. When Harry put it to him and Sid followed with, 'Back'ards every time, Sir. Didn't make any sense, did it, Billy?' Bossie fell into a long confusion about kinetics and resorted soon to small sarcasms about numbskulls and dolts. Anyway, all before him had witnessed it and he had not. It was foolish to have sought his aid.

The Living Pictures, in that sort, never came to the village again. The Great War and things as unforseen as the little engine had been saw to that.

BACK FROM AUSTRALIA

Hubert and Sid sat side-by-side on the garden wall bordering the street which ran below Sid's front garden. Elevated, it gave views all round and so of the cottages, similarly raised, on the far side of the road. It was a bright summer morning and they were making pop-guns. They regarded the shop-bought pop-gun as an inferior object. When you pushed its plunger it merely shot from its metal tube a cork attached to a string. Those they were making would eject proper projectiles at variable satisfactory distances. All the materials were provided by Nature.

For the tube a short length of straight ripe elderwood was required. This would be hollow like a gun-barrel after the soft, middle pith was pushed out. The plunger could be a straight piece of hazel fitting smoothly in the tube, the projectile a wild rose-hip, hips being now in full season. The hole running through the tube was of a size to allow a hip to fit firmly but not too tightly into the muzzle. The wad which the plunger pushed along to make the necessary compression would be well-chewed newspaper. A gun such as this could be made in little more than an hour, even allowing for some decoration and your initials cut into the side of the tube.

The boys worked first at removing the pith from their lengths of elder with pieces of stiff wire. All was quiet around them except that, opposite, Dobson's bitch, Spot, was busy burying something in the next-door neighbour's rose-bed. The gardens there sloped down to the street and were variously laid-out and tended. John Kemp's was by far the finest. Exactly ordered, with neat grass and formal flower-beds, it told of his work in the wider expanses at the big house. This morning he was away there and Mrs. Kemp indoors was quite unaware of the desecration openly enacted in the rose-bed.

Alert for interest should Mrs. Kemp appear, the boys watched as they worked.

Harry could not be with them. He had succumbed to mumps. Hubert and Sid were almost as sorry for him as he was for himself. In isolation in his bedroom this bright sunny morning, eating, drinking, smiling, only with the greatest difficulty even pain, he was in a sad plight.

'We'll make him a real good gun, when we've done these,' Sid said after a time.

'Yes,' Hubert agreed, 'We will and Florrie can give it to him. She's had the old mumps.' His tube, or barrel, now cleared of pith, he pointed it to the sky to see its interior shine as if glass-lined. 'That's all right,' he said. Then he pointed it as a telescope to the Kemps' garden, where Spot was now covering-in, and then he directed it along the village street.

'I say, Sid,' he said, 'what's on at Molly Wells's?' Molly, renowned gossip and purveyor of news, was a widow living alone half-way along. People were clustering at her gate. This was unusual and so interesting that Mrs. Kemp who had entered her garden at that moment, saw Spot off almost absent-mindedly, standing to watch, shading her eyes. The boys pocketed their knives, took up their half-made guns and dropped from the wall.

'Better see,' Sid said, 'Come on — run.'

'Who's that in the middle?' Hubert said, running neck and neck with him, 'folks are getting all round him. Something's on —let's get to see.' More and more people were gathering and now Mrs. Kemp came quite fast without hat, coat, or shawl.

A tall, elderly gentleman wearing a hat with an extraordinarily wide brim and peaked crown and in a suit of strange cut, stood surrounded by a group of Claydon's older people, animated much above the usual. He appeared to be joking and laughing, looked continually around, pointed his walking-stick at Tom Norman's waistcoat and then at George Norman's, next to all points of the compass, or so it seemed, laughing again and again. Then he pushed the hat far back on his head before removing it for a sort of general salutation, when he placed it under his arm.

Doors and gates opened on each side of the street and several elderly women hurried along, aprons discarded, tidying their hair with their hands, trotting to the group, making small excited exclamations. Bob Jennings, whose bachelor home was next to Molly's cottage, came hurrying down his garden-path, his hedge clippers in his hand, shouting, 'Strike me dead if it ent Joe Parsons! It's Joe come back!' The boys, quickly arrived, drew close, fascinated and puzzled. Molly had placed herself directly before the visitor looking flushed, talking excitedly, beaming at one and all. 'What's all the fuss, then, Hubert?' Sid whispered. 'Don't ask me, Sid,' Hubert murmured. 'Don't get in the way, then we might know,' so they stood back a pace or two, as other children came running to join them.

Joseph Parsons, of whom they had heard many tales which they dubbed ancient history each time they heard them, was paying a visit after an absence of more than thirty years. As a young man he had worked as an apprentice and then as a qualified craftsman in Harry's father's workshop. Len Wiggins often deplored the loss of him. But there had been nothing for it — young Joe must up and take his skills as a wheel-wright to Australia, leaving many a young bosom saddened, even blank, at his going. From his appearance this morning he had prospered. The thin, erect, strong figure had the poise and confidence of one who had seen and done much, who thought nothing of taking himself about the world, one used to taking things and people in hand.

Already there were by-standers taking pride from the fact that Claydon had reared this man. He shook hands all round, several times with some, saying to Bob, 'So you've travelled too? — South Africa, a bad business there. They got you, the Boers? Not too troublesome, the back? And you've got a little pension? We sat together in school, you say? It don't bear thinking how many years ago.'

Then he released Bob to say, 'Quaint, quaint, these old places!' — he meant the brick and timber cottages, the thatch, the leaded window-panes — Molly's, indeed, were latticed — the frilled lace-curtains and flowering geraniums behind them, declaring that all was much the same as thirty years ago, very much the same, as if Time had stood still.

Molly had moved close now looking more flushed than ever. Yes — he had been in the old country most of the summer staying with relatives; soon he would take ship home again, but he had been drawn today like a magnet for a last look at Claydon — bound to be the last, eh?

'Dear me, you mustn't say that!' Molly cried, 'there's years in you yet.' She had bunched her hair up and several times, had straightened her dress. 'Dear Joe,' she said, 'you've got to come in and have a cup of tea with me for old time's sake. Oh dear, how the years have flew!'

'Who's this young lady, then?' Joe laughed, pretending to look close. 'Upon my soul if it isn't Molly Stevens who was. That I will then, Molly. I'm here till five o'clock. Herb Wiggins — and how he's gone grey, will bring his wagonette for me at five to get me down to the station. And now, my dear young lady, let's take a look at you and you at me. Do you remember how we went to North Marston Fair together and what a long, long summer night that was with you and me singing we wouldn't go home till morning and you in bad trouble because we didn't? I see that very same smile, Molly - I see it again. But you've swelled, Molly, while I've shrunk — they say it's what Australia does to the men — but we mustn't, either of us, overdo that, Molly, must we!'

Peals of laughter followed this, Molly's by far the loudest, having body behind them. 'Remember!' she cried, 'course I do. That's a memory never to slumber. But you wear well, Joe, you really do. Family, Joe, tell us about your family.' 'That I will,' he responded and by this time Molly's hand rested on the sleeve of the suit, a very fine weave — smooth, almost silky and a nice grey. 'But first,' Joe went on, 'Tell me — the buildings next past my old school, that's now a house, what are they?'

'The hall and the new school,' Molly said.

'And White's old place at the Cross Tree Corner, it's gone and all is different there. He was a proper farming-man, with a clever wife, too — what's happened there?'

'Both passed on close to each other, nigh-on-ninety years a-piece,' George Norman said, eager always to satisfy a listener. He continued, 'Joshua Cole followed there — farmed the same way, you might remember Josh. When he died Sep Rigg took it on. Sep's missus had the chimney afire in the long drought and when the whole place burnt down old Josh's lost money was found in the brick chimney-breast. Never was such a to-do — all history now!'

'Well, that's how things are in this world,' Joe said, 'but' — and a hand to a pocket — 'look, folks, I've got photos to show you — family, my carriage-works and my staff in Adelaide,'

'Carriage-works, Joe?' — voices loud in unison. 'You

don't say! and a staff — there now!'

'Now look,' Molly said, 'and I won't hear nay from anybody, All come in to me and sit yourselves down in my front-parlour, while we brew tea. Come on Mrs. Kemp and Mrs. Wain, we'll serve tea all round for everybody to get together to see proper.'

Molly was excited, in her element and in the exactly right spot to know 'the latest', always an important matter with Molly. Her husband, an insurance agent who had travelled the villages, had been a wonderful asset in this. The house had fallen silent when he died, leaving her comfortably covered for her out-goings, but with a need to find her interests outside. As to family, she was all of it. So now, Molly leading, a move was made along her garden-path between her sky-blue larkspurs, the scent of her pinks and her love-lies-bleeding, all purple and sad, to her porch with the honey-suckle over it, mixing with John Wells's pink rambler. She opened her door wide: she need not to be ashamed of her house management. She took Joe by the elbow to lead him in, he bending his head to clear the lintel, the others following, most of them apologetic about being caught unawares in corduroys and work-boots, while Mrs. Polly Warner, laughing a little, begged that her coarse-apron be excused because, she said, of what lay underneath.

This development left the children standing in the street chattering like magpies, while Sid said, 'Golly — what a lot of old fuss!' 'Old stuff,' Hubert decided, 'and all because they went to school together, or something. If my Gramp hears about this Joe What's-his-name he'll come running too. Come on, Sid — Let's get our guns finished and then make Harry's. We'll get him a pocketful of hips too off the hedge. Harry hasn't missed much.'

However at that moment crusty old Jack Putt came hurrying to them, he whom the older boys regularly teased. Sid himself had been put into Jack's garden more than once with the gate held fast to the last second. Jack came in a mixture of hobble and trot with the aid of a walking-stick. All except Sid drew back to make way. 'Hurry up, Jack,' Sid called, 'You're just in time' and held the gate open, but he received no thanks. Waving his stick and hurrying through,

Jack growled, 'Out of my way, the lot o' you - give me room.'

Molly returned to her door-way and looked doubtful indeed, but called, 'Come on, Jack, if you mean to be sociable for once. Wonders will never cease' and when he hobbled up to her she hauled him in and closed the door. The children on this stood laughing, giggling and speculating, for Sid said, 'Old Jack never *went* to school — everybody knows that', while Hubert added, 'He'll put a damper on the proceedings,' which was an occasional observation of his mother's that he felt applied. The other children were already arranging in a small clamour to meet at the gate at five o'clock — 'case the old gentleman gives out all round, 'cos he looks rich, don't he?' and then they trickled away.

Hubert and Sid moved too to climb back to their seat on the wall. The brick-work was beautifully warm. There was no better place for their work and they resumed it at once.

The excitements at Molly's gate, the mysteries of her front parlour were as nothing in their renewed concentration.

'Harry's gun has got to be better than ours,' Hubert said, looking along the hazel which would be the plunger.

'Yes, we'll make it proper,' Sid agreed. After a period of silence and close work, he spoke again, 'Will you go back at five when Herb Wiggins comes to take the old gentleman to the station?'

'Might — might not,' Hubert replied, 'and now, look, I've been and *cut my finger*.'

OLD CONTEMPTIBLES

On a September morning one year before the great battles of World War One, Sidney Jennings, Harry Wiggins and Hubert Chapman from the Weir sat on the oak seat beneath the Cross Tree swinging their legs and contemplating the solemn fact that they were growing up, their total being twelve years, or nearly, each of them. Next year they could attempt the School Leaving Examination, the test in the three Rs which could in those days release you at thirteen years into the world of work.

'Reckon I'll have a go,' Sid said.

'I can't,' Harry said. 'I've got to stay till fourteen. My dad says I've got to follow on. He makes me paint the new wheel-barrows for a start.'

'*And* you've got your own tools and bench,' Hubert added.

'He calls that messing about,' Harry mused. 'He makes me do the barrows over twice, red inside, blue out, in the paint-shop.' And Hubert said, 'They say that test is dead easy.'

They sat where four roads met. *Up-the-Village* stretched ahead, in sight Webbs' general store, behind it Harry's father's carpentry and wheel-wright shops and next again his Uncle Herb's forge and just in view, the post office, brick, timber and thatch, strikingly unmodern. Further on lay, out of sight, Hubert's grandparents' home, the old school, the new village hall and library and the new school — after that fields and East Claydon. It was the main street.

To their left lay *Down-the-Village* more brief, which fell gently away past the non-descript farm-place called Wheelers', the homes of Harry and Sid and a few more cottages, also the pump which drew water from the well at the end of Well Lane. This road led on to Claydon Park and the Big House, and so to Middle Claydon and beyond.

The road to the right with no habitations, dropped steeply into the valley for the station, the long milk-trains and so for Aylesbury and London. Quiet though it was between high banks of hedgeside vegetation it had an importance, even an enticement about it, for it was the way folk went to 'branch out' and to see the world.

Behind the boys as they sat was the lane of the Weir people of whom Hubert was that morning the representative. So they sat at a true crossing, the centre where on summer evenings the men sat smoking their pipes putting the world to rights, above their heads and fastened to the elm's great girth, the parish notice-board for their local considerations. Before them was the wide grassy space where travelling salesmen in spring or summer laid out cheap china-ware for Dutch Auction, where an itinerant acrobat would trundle in to display his antics, where the barrel-organ man set up to let a child choose a tune and turn the handle for a penny. That and the road space beyond were ample and safe for children's games after tea until their mothers at last called them in.

The sun shone pleasantly and warmly on the three boys, but their spirits were low. The long holiday from school was ending fast. There was nothing more for them in the fields. Long hours, days, weeks of sunshine had seen the hay and corn gathered in record time. Some stacks were already thatched for winter. There was nothing whatsoever to abolish thoughts of the school bell, so soon to resume its call — 'in less than a week, Sid.' Their spirits were in their dangling boots.

Hubert's mother, Sally, had thought of several useful things he could be doing, 'Better than moping about — give the kitchen knives an extra scouring.'

'No,' he had said, 'let me do them same as usual Saturday morning. I'll do them twice as well. I'll go and see what Harry and Sid are doing' and what they were doing was nothing, if swinging legs is anything, or sorting out in desultory fashion, the handy, useful, or doubtful oddments in their jacket pockets. Twelve years each of them they had plenty of energy for instant use — see how they had used it in the hay and corn — if only they could think of something to do with it.

'I know,' Harry began, 'hazel nuts along the New Road, there's hundreds.'

'No good,' Sid said, at once, 'still green, nothing in 'em yet.'

'Well, *you* think of something then,' Harry grumbled.

So there they sat, the village apparently asleep but for the ring of Harry's uncle's distant anvil and sparrows squabbling in the dust almost at their feet.

'School next week,' Sid moaned. 'Can you believe it? might as well call it prison.'

'Don't talk about it,' the other two warned.

Then followed the longest silence of all, the sun's heat increasing every minute, the whole world it would seem at a standstill till Sid said, 'Well, we've got to think of *something*, haven't we?' It was at that moment that they heard it, a far-off purring sound, distant but clear.

'A motor-bike,' all three said together and they stood up.

'Coming our way,' Harry said. 'Listen!'

The sound had changed — urgent power, increasing every second. They ran for a view over the valley.

'Crossing the railway. Yes, he's coming this way. Look at the dust behind him!'

Soon he was at the foot of the hill then roaring up and climbing fast, no ordinary venturer this.

'Stand aside, boys!' they cried, 'give him room, give him a cheer!' and then he was on the rise, head down, goggles gleaming, the dust behind him billowing and pluming.

'Look how he's coming. He'll be past before we can see who it is. Give him a wave — give him a shout!'

They waved, they cheered as with a roar he passed, a figure all in brown, leather helmet, gleaming goggles, machine also brown. 'Golly,' they said, 'there's speed for you. He'll be down the village before you know.'

But there, wonder of wonders, they were wrong. There was a sudden silence. He had stopped feet down, pushing up his goggles, right before the Cross Tree.

'Come *on*!' cried Harry and through his falling dust they ran to him. Direction wanted, that was it. But no, he smiled, took a paper from a wallet on his belt, studied it, nodded, replaced it, pulled down his goggles, kick-started his machine, said, 'Sharp boys, I can see!' and was off again before either could find a word to say. Down the village he went and was gone. One or two mothers came too late, to their front gates, Wheelers' dogs barked and the boys stood in the road dumbfounded. Taking breath at last Hubert said, '*Army*, military. Didn't you see? And I said it first,' but he was not challenged, Sid saying, 'Didn't *you* see? He had a red arm-band.' 'Course I saw it,' Hubert said and Harry said, 'And I know what it means.'

'What? Quick, Harry — tell.'

'What my dad said — minoovers. Never, ever, thought they'd come this way.'

'Well, they mightn't anyway,' Sid said, wondering. 'What's minoovers, anyway?'

'Don't you *know*?' came Harry, 'training the army. That man was a dispatch-rider. They pick up sides and fight against each other for practice. If that chap was a Red there's Blues somewhere. Dispatch-riders go first, so where he came from that's where the other Reds will be. Come on — let's go and see.' 'Strewth — what are we in for, boys!' Sid yelled and they skipped and ran back to their view-point.

On the far side of the railway where first the rider was seen was a huge slow-moving mantle of dust.

'Golly, you're right, Harry,' Sid exclaimed, 'Look Hubert, there's thousands coming — thousands!'

'It's an army,' Hubert said, 'and it's coming our way. Reds they'll be and coming our way and we're the first to see 'em.'

'Ye-e-es,' they breathed, 'coming our way.'

The procession was now crossing the railway, heading right for the village, but what comprised it they could not see. Another single puff of dust was mounting the hill, another rider to roar past, non-stop, and be gone.

'His *colour*? shouted Sid, 'did you get his *colour*?'

'Red,' the others said, 'they'll all be Red, hundreds of 'em and Blues will be somewhere, you'll see.'

'Crikey!' they breathed.

The village was rousing, dogs barking 'all over town'. George Norman's snappy terrier, Tricks, was suddenly at their feet growling murderous things as George emerged from his cottage close by. Full of importance he said, 'Oh yes — either the Oxford & Bucks Light Infantry or the Yeomanry. I'd seen them from my garden — a full regiment I shouldn't wonder. Our Sid's with the Infantry. What do you think of that, young Sidney Jennings? Our Sid's a bombardier. This will make a fine how-do-you-do. A lot o' young chaps will fancy the King's shilling after this.'

His small imperial beard and bold good looks did not match his aged corduroy trousers, sagging waistcoat and collarless shirt. He directed his gaze down the hill.

'Mr Norman,' Harry ventured, 'if these are Reds where are the Blues? Did you know about the minoovers?'

'Oh, yes — I knew,' he said.

'He always knows everything,' Hubert whispered.

'Shut-up,' whispered Harry and aloud, 'Look, every-body. They're coming up the hill.'

There was now an audible rumble of wheels, of clattering hooves, of the tread of marching men. The head of the procession appeared above the rise. All four climbed the roadside bank; Tricks held by the collar was absolutely furious.

'The Blues?' Old George now said, knowingly, 'Over in Quainton Hills, waiting, I shouldn't wonder.'

'Is your Sid with these?' ventured Hubert, 'the Reds?'

'Or the Blues?' Sid added.

'Not for me to say,' George answered.

'He doesn't know. Shut-up, Hube — Shut-up both of you,' Harry whispered.

The procession was now close, coming with power and purpose and then passing — horse-drawn gun-carriages and limbers, wagons, field-kitchens, marching men in columns, all in the rough khaki, flat caps, puttees and hobnailed boots of the time, bandoliers, haversacks, water-bottles, rifles slung, their officers riding in calm command, polished to the last buckle. The Light Infantry or the Yeomanry? None could tell, but they were Reds to a man. Their vehicles, too, all had the same red splash. The hill surmounted to the last gun-carriage there then came loud orders and the line came to a halt. The boys stood transfixed and Old George hobbled back to view from his garden-gate, Tricks in grip growling and straining to get at the huge intrusive monsters, heels, in hundreds asking to be nipped, stamping in defiance of her — it was not to be borne.

The first dispatch-rider came roaring back for a brief discussion at the head of the line and then came command for horses to withdraw two wagons from the line, these to divert to the Cross Tree. On that came a magisterial pointing of a yellow cane. Straight ahead it was to be and to commands like gun-fire the column moved again, passing the Cross Tree heading down-the-village, mothers now out in force, children firmly gripped, as Wheelers' whippets made swift dashes at the nearest fetlocks, heels and wheels, retiring as swiftly with piercing yelps. Down the last slope and beyond the last habitations progressed the column, all boys available following within inches of the last wagon, regardless of danger and dust and in deep fear that they were to languish and fret in horrid emptiness while grossly undeserving distant others were favoured by a tremendous presence.

But no — sharp orders were heard down the line and then came a second halt and men descended to examine the wide grass verges, to open wide the field-gates at the New Road and to signal, 'Yes, this is the spot.' Foolish fears floated gently away. 'Come on,' Sid shouted, 'get to them to *see*!'

'No — the wagons at the Tree — don't forget them,' Harry urged. 'These are all right, we'll come back for them,' and off they sped at a gallop back to the seat at the Cross Tree, where, the wagons drawn up and the horses tethered, a tent was rising, a large square tent.

'Headquarters,' Hubert declared, 'Look at all these telephone wires rolled up and waiting.'

'Golly,' murmured Sid and Harry.

Busy men had the guy ropes fixed and the tent-pegs hammered down in no time. 'Each man's got his special job,' and as other children came running to the scene, 'Keep back — give 'em space,' Harry ordered.

'That's right, Sonny-boy,' one man said. 'You know how things go in war-time, I can see.'

'In war-time?' they queried in chorus.

'Best wait and see, eh?' he answered, smiling as he worked.

Next they ran land-lines from inside the tent with a pole hooking them up the tree, and so over the road to take them beside George Norman's garden, into his close and then out to the field on the edge of the hill, stopping at the thick screening hedge. Sid, Hubert and Harry followed them there for their every move. The view but for the hedge was over the whole valley and beyond.

'What did I say,' Harry said, 'this is to watch for the Blues.'

'Granborough, North Marston, Oving — that lot are bound to be Blues,' Sid added, with grim assurance, 'if they know we've got the Reds.' All agreed absolutely, also that the lot on the opposite slopes stood no chance whatever against the forces now at Claydon's command.

The men smiled as they laid ground-sheets behind the hedge and in the dry ditch below. They took binoculars from leather cases, adjusting, peering carefully between the hawthorn sprays and brambles.

'That's all then, boys,' said the man in charge, 'nothing more to see here. Off you go!'

It was a moment for tact and care. Harry gave Hubert a nudge. As politely as ever he had spoken anywhere, or at any time, and trying a smart salute, he said, 'Do you think we could come back later on, sir, just to watch you? We wouldn't get in your way. We'd do just what you say, sir — just for a little while after tea?' Of course, they had the distant hills in mind. Surely a great and mysterious army was there. It gave Hubert a surprising power of speech.

'Better join-up first,' the man replied, seeming to agree. 'You're all in mufti, though.'

'Join-up!' — the words rang in their heads like a clarion-call.

'Thank you, sir, we will,' all three cried as one. Swiftly they ran — it was a running sort of day — Sid saying, 'Mufti? What's that?' and Harry, '*Come on* — there's no time for talk.' A great urgency was upon them. Their personal rifles! Why had no-one thought of them with Harry's dad's carpentry shop, spare wood and Harry's own bench of tools ready and waiting? They sped there and never were three rifles more swiftly made. For once Sid and Hubert worked without one thought of the coffin lids and boards, with their worrying shapes, stacked beside them along with new wheel-hubs, felloes, shafts and planking. The smell of resin and saw-dust all-pervading and three efficient weapons to be the same in size and style precluded even that thought. Harry's father looked in, 'You will need slings. Use these old horse-reins. Careful with the edged tools. Hands behind the work. We don't want any walking-wounded before battle, do we?'

'Thanks, dad,' Harry said looking up, for a moment intensely surprised. Len Wiggins smiled, just as he worked, in slow, careful fashion. This heavy, clever, often taciturn man who could build huge, beautiful hay-wagons, who was not much given to smiling, was he wishing he were a boy again, young and slim, like Harry? The reins, cut for slings, were exactly right for their feverish work.

Next requirement, arm-bands — they ran again, rifles slung. For Hubert red hair-ribbon was graciously lent by his sister Eva, for Sid and Harry strips were torn from an old red-flannel petticoat by Sid's laughing mother, 'Looks like emergency. Here, have nice wide pieces. How did I ever come to wear it!' She was a jolly sort of mother. 'For mercy's sake be careful,' she called as off they ran again, 'What a to-do it all is! Bless their hearts, they're all worked-up already!'

They were now of the soldiery. There was a notable straightening of young male backs, a scorning of almost all girls. One or two of the tom-boy sort, Daisy Warner perhaps, might be allowed in, but the tests would be stringent. They would have to provide their own rifles.

The men at the Cross Tree were now settled. There was a telephone on the table inside the tent and a man sat there with papers. A map was pinned up behind him. The outside men were friendly, even jolly, as they gave the recruits a smart look-over. They stayed the same unless their officers were around. They, when they suddenly arrived, seemed quite unable to see the boys, although at every suitable moment each one made a point of saluting in correct style at attention.

Towards evening they examined the main body. They savoured the tempting smells of the field-kitchens, saw the watering, feeding and grooming of the tethered horses, the tents in exact lines, ventured a little towards the tent for officers. The gun-carriages, limbers and wagons were all drawn together, sentinels pacing beside them. However, for Harry, Sid and Hubert the stronger pull was to the out-post on the hillside. They had joined-up promptly. Those men should see that polite country boys had resource and the spirit to put them in the vanguard anywhere.

They made their way to them again, following the

land-lines on tip-toe, rifles slung, to be suddenly and startlingly challenged by a real rifle put firmly to the first of the chests, Harry's, who at once stepped back on Sid's foot.

'Friend — friend — friend,' they answered together.

'Phew!' Sid said, and the big man smiled down. All was well. They 'advanced, friends, to be recognised' and entered dreamland. Screened by the hedge was the field telephone and prone on ground-sheets two men had binoculars directed to the far hills. In the dry ditch below in a cosy hide lay a resting man. Lowering himself in, the smiling sentry said, 'Our bivvy. Get right down low, boys.' Yes — they took turns watching, that was the ticket. Carefully all three boys pointed. 'Enemy over there?' they whispered.

'Thousands,' the reclining man said, 'heads down.'

'Crikey!' Sid exclaimed, 'knew that Marston lot would be Blues,' but if the watchers saw any they said nothing.

Harry gave Hubert another nudge. Boldly and politely as before, he whispered across to them, 'Could we, please — would it be allowed for us to see, if we are ever so careful and do what you say, sir?'

The nearer man said, 'One at a time, then. One peep each.' They were good sorts, friendly, a bit like most boys.

Hubert was first because he had asked. How heavy those army field-glasses were, how gently the big man adjusted them for him and with what an astounding leap North Marston came into view from across the valley. There was a man digging up potatoes in his garden and his wife was filling a basket, two dogs were chasing each other on the green, a woman was lifting the top of a bee-hive and the church clock said twenty-past-six. He moved the glasses right and left.

'I can't see any enemy,' he whispered.

'Course not — they're not fools,' the man said. The other chuckled, 'They know we'd know if they moved a finger.'

Harry and Sid took their turns, trembling with rapture.

'It *is* Reds against Blues, isn't it?' Harry asked.

'Something of the sort,' came a reply. 'How do you know about the Blues?'

'Guessed,' Harry said, 'Well — it's what people say.'

'Some smart recruits here,' said the smiling man. 'Big

Page 101

things on tomorrow. What ammunition do you use?'

Somehow they hadn't given it a thought.

'Better be dead certain by the morning,' the resting man advised.

'Do you only fight in the day-time?' Hubert asked.

'Depends,' he replied, his thumb pointing Marston way. 'Reckon it'll be in daylight, though. And now what about supper and bed, hey? Your mums will be out looking for you.' They said they supposed they should go, though the allure of the cosy bivvy was growing more powerful with every minute. With the far hills turning misty and the evening dew beginning to rise they withdrew their forces; but from Hubert came one more question, 'Will you be here all night?'

'All night, Sunny Jim,' said the smiling man, 'What a one this boy is! Down with you — flat and crawl till you get into the road again.'

'Goodnight, sirs. Thank you very, very much, sirs,' they said as they puffed, wriggled and scrabbled to stretch weary legs in the shelter of the road.

Big things tomorrow, but directly ahead and waiting were sharp chidings about meals missed or delayed and then bolted, also about the state of one's clothes, especially elbows and knees, and then heavy scrubbings before any chance of supper. Sleep was instant unconditional surrender.

In the morning, even before breakfast, there were sensations — pillion-riders, galloping horses, hauling gun after gun, limber after limber, down Weir Lane, past the Weir houses, past the farm-house and out into the Bernwood fields to be placed behind Fred Lester's tallest and thickest hedges on the hill's highest ridge, gun muzzles screened and pointing over the valley.

Soon began a pounding which shook hips, haws, wild crabs and brambles to sorry rags, to scatter sheep and cattle to the fields' farthest extremities. Polly the donkey, and Emily the cob, and the turkey-cock retired to the remotest corner of the paddock, ears back, nostrils and wattles aflare, to stare, stamp and gobble in deepest alarm.

'Only blanks,' every-one said, but oh — the quivering excitements, the glorious thumpings while the Bernwood people grew in apprehension every minute.

'Be careful, you boys, urged the fathers. 'Army people stand no nonsense. You can't help, so don't hinder,' just as Sally said to young Hubert, 'And if you are not in for proper meals this day, whatever may be going on, you will get nothing,' and she meant it for certain.

Allied to this turmoil, on and off through the day, groups of infantrymen scampered about the village and into the fields, dispatch-riders came and went and several times gleaming motor-cars brought important men in grand uniforms and shining leggings to gather at the Cross Tree tent, amidst massive salutings, to talk quickly together and then go — Reds, by their special flashes, every one.

So far, the boys had seen no sign of anything blue, eastward, right, left, centre, anywhere. Redness was all.

They early decided to adhere to their own kind, the infantry, the foot-soldiers. When they fell prone, their rifles at the ready, all three boys at a careful distance, dropped too to give them supporting fire, 'five rounds rapid', just as they. In return there was reward, rich spoils scattered in the grass, in the dry ditches, at all firing positions, beautiful spent cartridge-cases of brass or copper. If one were quick in the follow-up one too hot to handle was a rare prize. All smelt delightfully of burnt gun-powder.

'Wait till we get to school with these,' Harry said, 'the dinner kids from Middle Claydon and Verney haven't any chance of these.'

'They'll want to bargain, for sure,' Sid asserted, gloating over his cache.

By mid-afternoon there was no more firing. The artillery returned to base, the infantry too withdrawing and there followed a quiet unreal, even strange. The boys went to proper teas and Hubert was required to go early to bed lest he should be fatigued to death. But sleep would not come, because, well — what of tomorrow? There was no instantaneous sleep anywhere in the village that night. Only when darkness had long fallen and the last bugle call down-the-village had died away did Hubert nod, too tired then even to wonder what the morning would bring.

It brought astonishment and a weird emptiness. George Norman stood at the Cross Tree addressing a knot of grown-ups and children standing where the headquarters tent had lately been. That, the tethered horses, the two wagons, the land-lines — all had vanished. As the three wondering boys hurried to the scene George was saying, 'They went at first light — they're with the others now — all packing up to be gone.' His beard wagged up and down with his usual importance, 'We ought to know what it's all about if we read the daily papers. Our Sid, when he was home on leave, said as how the Germans are building up on land and sea to get at us, even if that Kayser is the king's own cousin. That's what this is all about. The military, both sides, take no account of the likes of us.'

'Well, we've seen it on our own door-steps,' Jimmy Warner commented, to a general murmuring. Equipped for further fray the boys stood suddenly lost, so Harry shouted, 'The Blues, Mr Norman, what about the Blues? Will they come next?'

'The Blues?' he laughed, 'Bless the boy, they were pounded to nothing yesterday, you might have known that.' They stood dreadfully puzzled. 'Come on,' Sid said, deciding to leave, 'let's go and see 'em packing up. He'll be on to Inkerman next, how his uncle beat the Russians, about a hundred years ago in the Crimean War!' Slowly they went.

By noon every vestige of Red had left, continuing westward, leaving the village as bemused by the peace left to it as by the intrusion that had stirred it to boiling-point. 'Left it all tidy as they could,' observed the wondering folk, 'shut all the gates. The ground's not much cut up considering.' Well, it was the season which all great armies have preferred for their movements, the harvests in, the earth sun-dried, beaten hard, not yet re-ploughed.

The de-mobilised three ambled back to the view-point where they and the watching men had lain. 'This was the best bit,' Harry said, and all agreed, slowly returning then to the Cross Tree seat. Old George and his audience had all gone home. They unslung their rifles and removed the arm-bands to sit somewhat as before till Sid said, 'What about it, then?' rattling the treasure in his pocket.

'That's it,' Harry said, 'share out all equal. Empty 'em all out on the seat, all pockets inside out and share out!'

They turned them out, a shining heap. In strict rotation they chose and there they lay in three lesser heaps. Harry, by a small seniority, claimed the odd one, of course.

'Wait till we get to school with these,' he gloated again. 'What shall we say — one for a blackie's egg, two for a pigeon's, what?'

'Three for a pheasant's, I reckon,' Sid said and Hubert, 'How many for a plover's then? We've got to work it all out.' They got down to business. School could begin as soon as convenient.

Tariffs done, they sat as on the first morning until Sid said, 'I'm going home to show mine and make a list,' strolling away, hugging his spoils. After a long silence Hubert said, 'I've thought of something, Harry — our ship, our liner, it's nearly made. These cartridges, all brass, would look all right fixed on standing up and a drop of paraffin in each one and a bit of string for a wick to have her out on the pond all lit up and looking real when it's dark?'

'You're right,' Harry agreed, standing up. 'She's nearly made. That's something to do all right.' They set out at once for the carpentry shop, guns sadly at trail.

She was just as they had left her when the hay-work began way back in June long before the coming of the manoeuvres, the two-feet length of floor-board, shaped fore and aft, the block of wood for super-structure, the ship's rail of one-inch nails and carefully entwined string.

'She only needs funnels. Find a bit of dowel — too thin. This old wheel-spoke, no — too thick, this bit of broom handle then — just right.' Very soon, rough but ready, she stood complete but for her brass. Twelve from Harry's store for starboard, twelve of Hubert's for larboard, but how to fix them?

'We can't bore holes for them to stand in, it would take years,' Harry pondered, 'got to be fixed somehow. How can we make 'em stand?'

'I've got an idea, Harry,' Hubert was feeling a cartridge. 'Look, feel yours, they've all got rims. Three tin-tacks to hold each one down, Harry. We can make 'em stand up like that.'

'Hoo-ray, you've got it!' Harry cried. 'Come on —

Emmy Webb's shop for some tin-tacks. I've got some pocket money left. Pay your share Saturday.'

Patient tapping in of the tacks, turns in holding and fixing and two sore thumbs, saw her standing grandly ready for her voyaging. No thought was given to paint-work, she must be got to the water. 'I can persuade my mother about paraffin,' Hubert said, 'and a lamp-funnel for filling.'

At that moment Sid came in. 'Coo — what's on, boys?' and after Harry had explained, 'Golly — to *America* all lit up! I'll help. We want a nail front and back to tie strings so we can pull her across and back again.'

'Fore and aft is what you mean,' Harry said, 'for ships.'

'Do I?' Sid said 'Anyway, I've got the string from my kite at home — won't be long' and off he went at a gallop.

'We've got to have him,' Harry grumbled. 'Besides, I haven't got any string.'

'Nor have I,' Hubert said. 'We'll make him be careful. He'll want to pull because it's his string.'

They carried her carefully past the waters of the Weir Pond and set her down by the back-door in the yard for negotiation with Hubert's mother.

'What an idea,' she laughed. 'All right. Have the small funnel and do it right away from the house, if you please — far back on the stones, for safety's sake. String for wicks? And my scissors, I suppose, too.' She found string and cut the twenty-four wicks.

'She's a sport,' Harry whispered.

'Course she is,' Hubert said. 'She likes a bit o' fun.'

'Can't see my mum doing it,' murmured Sid, 'too busy talking.'

The filling was a slow and delicate business before a sceptical audience. 'We're coming to see her sink,' one said. There was a firmness about matches which would be allowed only at launching. Whatever would we think of next! — lift her carefully, keep her level.

They got their vessel to the water's edge as the sun was going down. The whole stretch of the weir was placid as if waiting. Sid fastened his strings fore and aft.

'I'm in charge of the matches,' Hubert said. 'My mum said.'

'We take turns lighting,' Harry insisted.

'And pulling,' Sid said. 'Let's do it before anybody comes. Let's be the first to see her.' All agreed, 'Yes, let's be the only ones.'

'She's ours, anyway,' Harry said, 'mine and Hubert's — we made her, don't forget.'

'And my string,' Sid claimed, firmly holding the aft string.

'All right — your string. Let's get her lit,' Hubert said.

Harry removed his jacket to shelter her against the rising breeze and the lighting began. One by one the wicks flared up, then settled till all, though wavering, were secure and even and reflecting in the water.

'What a sight, boys,' they breathed together. 'Push her out gently. Gently does it. Let your string out, Sid.'

Hubert had the fore-string to ease her out and now the breeze helped her smartly to the middle where she stopped against the strings, an enchanting sight. Dusk had quite fallen. Her reflections doubled the wavering twinklings of her lights. She was an amazing watery will-o'-the-wisp.

'This is worth something, boys,' Harry said yet again, 'and we thought it out ourselves. Now me for the string to pull her right across. Let yours go, Sid.'

Smoothly, almost mysteriously, she responded to make her virgin crossing, heaving-to for a close view on the far shore.

'Now I pull her back,' called Sid.

'Pull then,' Harry called in return, 'ever so gently — not how you mostly do things.'

'Shut up, you,' came his voice sharply across the water, but Sid pulled with infinite care to make it the first ocean crossing aft to fore. They let her idle once more off-shore to take in the full wonder of her. She rocked a little as the wind rose and then, suddenly, one of her lights flickered and died.

'The oil's using up. Pull her in, Sid.'

Sid pulled and as the two ran to him more of her dancing lights, one by one, sank and failed. They got her to the shore as her last flame flickered, flared up, sank and was no more.

'Never mind, boys,' Harry said. 'Get her up on the bank. Worth it, eh? Jolly well worth it and all because of the soldiers.'

They sat down beside her in the darkness which had rapidly enfolded them. The night breeze rose pushing strongly at their backs and at the lapping water at their feet. Harry had a hand on her wet prow.

'We made her, Hubert,' he said.

'Yes, we made her,' he said quietly.

'What did I say?' Sid said quietly. '*America!* America is what I said. Didn't I?'

Over on the water, far over, was their picture of her, lit from stem to stern, her reflection dancing with the now dancing waves, another record crossing done, awaiting her the acclaim of the multitude on the shore and she signalling to draw in.

THE GOOD SERGEANT

No village boy could claim a father anything like Sergeant Frank Daniels, the caretaker at the village hall, library and games rooms. Alice who so often visited the Yard, smiled as the children spoke over and over again, of the frightening moment when with one sweep of his sword, before the hall full of people, he had severed the apple resting on her neck.

'Calm is what you have to be, and trusting,' she said, 'or everything would go wrong. No danger really. He could chop an apple on the kitchen-table without making a mark. But that's nothing to what he can do with a sword.'

They shuddered. They knew he had seen service in foreign fields where were unaccountable people like dancing dervishes, yelling warriors with huge hide shields, frightening spears and wicked assegais and treacherous Pathans always making trouble. Mentally they saw him in the midst of wild affrays coldly smiling as he carved, evaded and thrust, because the printed pictures of battle scenes in the far outposts of the Empire were like this, crowded with gleaming slashing swords and spears, men in scarlet uniforms, fallen horses and ferocious 'natives'.

Boys set about making wooden swords throughout the village — cutlasses, scimitars, some with jewelled hilts set with gems spared from their sisters' bead-boxes, glued in. The simple wearing of one straightened the back, firmed the facial expression and added to the height.

The Yard claimed the sergeant as an unchallengeable connection. Son-in-law to Granny and Will he often strode through patting heads as he passed, to do a quick job for them in house or garden, for he was also a brisk handyman. Also when Lancer Fred was home on leave he came to gather the latest news and views on army matters. Heads nodded solemnly, laughter and banter were frequent and Granny would call, 'Oh dear me, that can't be true!' with Will shaking his head to say, 'They're men of the world, right enough — that yarn should be told to the Marines.' The military men would then march smartly off together, purpose or mission unrevealed. No other village conclave had two such men to enliven it, men who personally extended, set and then held the bounds of empire.

In charge at the village hall, his years of service done, the sergeant had been a leading drill instructor, so his physical strength, prowess, gymnastic and weaponry skills gave him unusual authority in the recreation rooms. He ensured quiet reading and perusal in the reading-room and remarkable order in the diverse uses of the hall. The braced figure and direct eye suddenly there but watching only, would bring a hush even to the games room where the rowdiest elements usually gathered, while the billiard room was a place of peace whether he was there or not, save for the click of the balls and the murmur as Archie Foskett potted the red yet again like a cannon-shot.

'Quite the best man ever at the hall,' pronounced the village, 'years of good in him yet — strong as a horse, lissom as a cat and always on the job. Ready for a joke too and a pot of ale without overdoing it. He's taking on some Council land for rearing a few calves and for hay. The army's loss is our gain, all can see. He's a reservist, so we're told.'

The squire and his wife, whose auspices and efforts had provided the hall premises and amenities only a few years before, swiftly saw his value, finding him apparatus for drill and gymnastic classes which, sparse and tentative at first, grew to be successful beyond ordinary village competence. The hall became a centre of activity four evenings a week.

On the two ladies' evenings small boys pressed to the open door or stood on the window-sills to peer and to be amused and then astonished. There on the stage was the sergeant in sharp military trousers, singlet and tennis-shoes, his close-cropped head held high, short moustache fiercely brushed, wielding dumb-bells in graceful swingings and curves in time with Alice at the piano, setting the pace for the two files on the floor of earnestly concentrating mothers, aunts and elder sisters, whose efforts to follow and to emulate varied from delighted assurance right down to despair and bewildered disgust.

'Never mind, ladies, if at first we don't succeed — hey? Take a rest and watch me. Let the weight in the bell do the work — that's the secret. After two, Alice!' Alice thumped and he swung to smiles, sighs, giggles and murmurs of,

'Never shall I do it, Lizzie,' or, in a wicked whisper, 'Could do with one of these at home,' when the sudden laughter brought a sharp call from the stage, 'Concentrate, ladies — concentrate, *if you please*.' How determined they looked in their white blouses, long skirts, shortened just a little, their hair-bands and rubber shoes as he stopped to say, 'Once more then — swinging only, positions thus. Now Alice — one, two and go!' — this time for a swinging as one.

'Look at our Gwen,' Sid Jennings chuckled on the window-sill, 'she'll crack herself on the back of her head in a minute. This is as good as the circus any day' and another watcher, 'That's my mum right at the front. He's got her for leader. I can't believe it.'

They pressed their noses to the panes, jostled at the door waiting for the exercise they never missed — the bar-bells, for then the earnest ladies puffed and thrust in piston-work equal to a rally of steam-engines. The watchers ached with suppressed laughter, but good came of it, no doubt of that. Some in the village, not drawn in, thought it a nine-day wonder, a novelty unlikely to last, to which wild horses would not drag them.

'At the Village Hall — Swedish Drill for Ladies, Tuesday and Thursday Evenings, 7.30 sharp to 9.0 p.m.' announced the village notice-board. 'Gymnastic Classes for Men, Wednesday and Fridays — same place, same time. Proper dress, enthusiasm and six-pence per evening the only requirements. Apply to Sergt. F Daniels, or to Mrs Clara Daniels, Caretakers' Quarters'.

The men's evenings saw boys gathered at doors and windows in even greater numbers. The sergeant led in every exercise — vaulting-horse, parallel-bars, hand and climbing ropes, the young men aspiring, perspiring, grunting and triumphing in a scene of continuous thumps, bumps, exhortations and cries which had his small audience jigging with envy and desire, now with never a giggle, never a foolish laugh. Only young men came for this, no older men. Physical effort had been their lot for years. Wives could loosen up muscles if they wished and look ridiculous like a bunch of school-girls, so long as there remained a proper regard for clean shirts, washing-up and supper-times. Let the young fellows do it while still lithe.

So the young men did press-ups, vaulted, tumbled, tried single combat, climbed and gritted teeth, finding they had muscles and agilities that could achieve exercises, set-pieces, even pyramids, as the sergeant demonstrated, encouraged, eased up and over, smiled and said whoops! More and more boys stood at the doors and always now a cluster of village girls gathered, elbowing a little and closely watching.

The ladies who persisted grew ever more practised. They advanced to the crossing of hands and finger-twirling, and with their bar-bells could execute the 'chain'. Girls as well as boys approved, no giggling now, all serious. 'It's a knock-out,' said George Norman, 'an eye-opener!' When the notice-board added, 'Boys' Half-hour also Weds. and Fri. 7.00 to 7.30 p.m. Min. age 12 years, three pence only each session. Apply as above', Sid Jennings, Harry Wiggins, Fred Guntrip and young Hubert of the Yard joined at once in a state of high fever.

That man's palm in the small of the back as a boy forward-rolled over the high horse, the ability to walk the bar, the four of them without a wobble, spurred them to quite outrageous boasting at home and school. But it was true enough that all four succeeded in swarming up the climbing-ropes hung from within a yard of the hall ceiling, true also that the sergeant climbed up to Harry to take him on his shoulders and then descend the rope with him, his arms outstretched, gripping only with his knees, saying quietly as they sank to the mat below, 'Smile, laddie — smile and wave!' Harry clung, smiled and waved, 'Because I'm the thinnest' he explained.

The advanced squads performed at the Liberal Demonstrations and the wedding and christening celebrations of the Big House lawn and electrified the village socials, hush and cheers alternating in his insistently demanded sword-play. The slicing of Alice's apple, was perhaps the most alarming, although three glinting swords in the air at once were enough and to have two of them, as finale, spinning by their hilts on his extended fore-fingers and the third in his mouth, like a pirate's cutlass, brought applause which had more than a spice of relief in it.

Smiling broadly he would produce a broom-handle and ask members of his audience to examine it. Were there flaws in it? Was it tough and sound all through its length? 'Solid all through, Sergeant — no knots and a good straight grain.' Dick and Len, two of his gymnasts, then stepped to the stage to sit in chairs facing each other the broom-stick's length apart, each holding horizontal an open razor, its edge uppermost, pointing these towards each other at the same height. On each blade the Sergeant then carefully hung a small loop of paper, such as children used for paper-chains at Christmas. Then with even more care he inserted each end of the broom-stick into its paper loop and there fragilely it hung, Dick and Len thus supporting it, sitting tense and still. 'You see,' he said then, turning to his audience, 'how the broom-handle is suspended quite level and how it is held at each end. I propose cutting it in clean halves with my sword without disturbing Dick or Len, or the razors or even the paper loops.'

His audience stirred and craned to see, boys jostled for position, their mothers murmured, 'Dear me! What next with this man?' and their fathers, 'This beats me, no doubt there's a trick in it.'

'My sword please, Alice,' he said and Alice brought forth the long straight blade, the apple-cutter. Some shivered as he took it to look along its length which gleamed as he raised it standing a little back from the centre of the broom-stick, measuring his distance. That right he brought the sword down lightly touching the centre as if mentally marking a spot. Then, face set and eyes on that spot, he raised the blade again, high and straight this time, and brought it down in one swift stroke for the stick to clatter in halves to the stage-floor. The audience gasped and Dick and Len rose removing the loops from their razor-blades, showing them, fragile though they were, to be quite intact.

'Take them down for folk to see,' Daniels said, handing down also the severed pieces, 'Look — a clean-cut, no trick.' 'Give him a clap!' came a general cry and everyone cheered and the hobble-de-hoys at the back whistled. As Alice carefully removed the sword someone said, 'He should ha' bin on the proper stage. What next shall we see?' but another, 'My God! Think of a hundred men charging at you with swords like that-un!'

In a very different enterprise, he took a party of

younger children to the party of parties when the squire and his lady invited a hundred children of the Claydon villages to a Christmas tea and entertainment in their high North Hall. The party travelled in high excitement in a conveyance of the sergeant's own contriving. For more than a week he worked on one of the Bernwood Farm hay-wagons, brought to his yard for the fitting of seats and the building of a great wooden frame with canvas covering to make a shelter for those who would ride. They thrilled when he said he would hang lanterns in it because they would go in the dusk and come home in the dark, but they worried dreadfully when he said that he would take twenty only and no fat ones, so some measuring would have to be done. Well, he had been a sergeant in the army — they had to abide by it and be humble. In fact everyone said 'Yes, Sir' to practically everything he said as they watched and he whistled, sawed and hammered away. Two days before the party and, as school closed, he finished and then snow began to fall, the kind which stays crisp and even and blindingly white. The big shire, also from Bernwood, dear old Darling, white like old snow, would pull the wagon with frost nails put in her shoes, by Harry's uncle at the forge.

At four o'clock on the great day dusk was already falling, but the snow had stopped as, at the Cross Tree, the riders were lifted, bubbling with excitement, to their seats, measuring quite forgotten, it seemed, for the sergeant just hummed merrily, saying, 'Up we go, snuggle up together' as two laughing teachers also climbed in. Eyes dazzled. Three hanging storm-lanterns cast a glow over the company, just as the sergeant had said, but also he had hung paper-chains, holly and ivy all over the inside of the shelter. Mothers and fathers waved as he took up the reins, sitting tall and straight with holly berries in his hat, a most secure driver. Darling knew it, for she stepped off smartly at once. The children settled together under their rugs for an adventure not one of them could ever have imagined.

'Lead us in one of your songs, Miss Bradley' called the sergeant, after a while, the village left behind. 'Yes,' she said, 'Our special song for the party. Altogether children' and she led with *Bring a torch, Jeannette, Isabella — bring a torch to the stable, do!* They sang other carols and they peeped round the canvas to see the wagon's lights reflecting on the snow and they called to the walkers and other riders chatting and laughing, all going their way; but they went quiet when Darling reached the long avenue of ancient trees which led to the House, a dark and solemn place. However, they took courage and sang loudly *God rest you merry, Gentlemen*, the sergeant and teachers helping so strongly that Darling thought she must hurry, getting there, right on time, to join a jolly concourse in the courtyard just as the doors opened in a flood of light where their host and hostess stood, smiling to welcome them. Slowly they made their way in, teachers leading, the sergeant at the rear like a shepherd with his flock.

Throughout that wonderful evening he played a part. He performed sword exercises on the stage, but with fire-tongs and shovels, which brought him laughter and cheer after cheer. He organised a huge game of Pass-the-Parcel, then Musical Chairs and after that he arranged the chairs, giving sharp military orders, into their positions at the long loaded tea-tables. He gave the commands for the firing of the crackers lying beside the plates, 'Place your hands on your crackers. I shall give the word to pull — not yet, not yet, young sir! The word will be *pull* after I count three. Are you ready? Are you ready?' — and how like a full sergeant-major he looked — 'Then grip those crackers hard for my one-two-three and *pull!*' and a tremendous crackling bang it was.

He helped to find the presents on the tallest and most brilliant Christmas tree ever seen, he arranged the company round it at the end as the lights were lowered for the children to sing the two carols specially learned in school to be their way of thanking Sir Harry and Lady Rachel, their children, their friends and helpers, first *Bring a torch, Jeannette, Isabella* — and next the older children's *Wassail, wassail to our town* —. The teachers made little speeches of thanks after that and the sergeant called for the mightiest of cheers as their hosts stood to wave good-bye, the stars twinkling in thousands overhead as Darling took her happy load away.

They sang their way home, those who could stay awake, Darling taking them steadily on, their presents tightly held, the lanterns swaying above their heads, the sergeant, straight as a ram-rod, joining in. The next day would be

Christmas Eve and snow began to fall again for clouds now covered the stars as he and Darling took all children safely to their homes.

The sergeant's gymnastic classes stopped altogether for a long break every summer. The hay and corn had to be got in and men and boys were needed in the fields full-time. The sergeant also, as a part-time husbandman, must make sure of winter-feed for his calves. By the last summer of peace in the year 1913 after the harvest ended came the autumn of the army manoeuvres which had driven Harry, Sid, Hubert and other boys all over the North Bucks countryside, into a state of feverish energy. For three whole days the military had centred on the village. Brisk indeed then were the sergeant's movements, jolly his chats with off-duty personnel, keen his eye and thoughtful his mien as the invaders set about their business in the fields, on the hill-side, in camp. Asked for a professional opinion on the military management he said, 'Smart — very smart. I can't fault them. The old country will have nothing to fear if we have plenty more like them.'

'Expect you're right,' said the questioner, 'being a military man and a reservist yourself.'

After the intruders withdrew the sergeant's hall sessions resumed as popular as ever. If some older ladies retired saying enough was enough, they were at once replaced by more than ready younger ones.

By next June the sergeant's squads had reached new peaks of achievement without a hint of any kind that all was about to end, that within two months there would be Declaration of War against Germany, that immediately after that the manoeuvrers of 1913 would be battling against overwhelming force in Belgium and then in France and that, suddenly, the sergeant himself would be gone.

'Called to the colours, first thing,' the village said, 'and half a dozen of his young gym chaps have volunteered to go with him.' The whole country now was serious, apprehensive, avid for news. 'German onslaught halted thirteen miles from Paris,' proclaimed the newspapers in their blackest headlines, 'the Allied lines hold.' This was after weeks of harrowing battle.

George Norman stood at his cottage gate, his three

daily newspapers laid out on the top bar, neighbours gathered round him, all convinced that Frank Daniels, immediately made Sergeant-Major, and George's Sidney, bombardier, had had a hand in the tremendous grinding halt before which Paris trembled and millions paled, holding breath.

'Daniels,' George declared, '— here, take the papers, it's put plain what I've said all along about the Germans — Frank Daniels and our Sid, much the same build, all hard muscle both of 'em and ready to put the fear of God into any German, man to man. Put Sid in the old uniform and he'd be the image of my uncle who fought at Inkerman. He was a George, too. The Germans had got it all planned, but they'll have such as our two to reckon with before Christmas. It can't last longer than that, now they're stopped.'

The German Emperor was denied his triumphal ride into Paris, but, the enemy lines pushed back at huge cost, the Western Front formed to become a morass stretching from the North Sea shore to the frontiers of Switzerland, the Hindenberg Line, a barrier of concrete and wire, standing impregnable until summer 1918, despite Verdun, the Somme, the Ypres Salient, Paschendaele, Hill 60. Other Claydon men left for the forces and by 1916 several had fallen. By that time a heavy dread had fallen over all Western Europe, the casualty lists growing daily longer, frustration and bitterness growing with them. 'Well, George,' someone said heavily, 'what was it you said about the war ending by Christmas 1914?'

'It's the generals,' George replied, 'our generals, not the Germans. We started as if it was the Boer War all over again. The Germans banked on it. God knows how it will end now. It'ull need all the Americans can send us. It's a question of who gives' and he turned away.

Occasionally field-postcards were delivered to the village. All were the same, whether to the caretaker's quarters at the hall, or to the cottage near the Cross Tree, saying only that the sender was in good health, as certified by Field Post Office, signifying that at the time of the minimal writing the warrior was safe from harm, but village apprehension was continuous and increased daily.

One morning, probably in early spring, 1917, George stood at his gate again and long before his breakfast-time, his neighbours hurrying to him in wonderment and concern. Never before had anyone seen him in any sort of perturbation, but now his hands were shaking, his features pale through the imperial whiskers, his shirt-sleeves loose and unrolled, boots unlaced, his house-door ajar, swinging unheeded.

'Sure you didn't dream it, George? Look, there's not a cloud in the sky and the birds are singing — they'd have gone quiet. You dreamt it, George.'

'Not I,' he said. 'You can't dream a thing like that. I tell you it shook me straight out of my sleep, not a quarter of an hour ago it was — like a thunder-clap, like an explosion. I could swear the window rattled. I sat straight up in bed — my clock stood at half after seven. Somebody here must have heard it.'

'Well, nobody here heard anything,' said one and another. 'That makes it a deep mystery, if you ask me,' observed another, 'unless you thought you were out after conies with your gun, half asleep and half awake, like.'

'Oh no, when I sleep I sleep right through. No mystery at all,' he said grimly. 'I know as clear as clear can be what it means — something bad about our Sid in France. I've had a message and I reckon it's pretty bad. No thank you, Jimmy. I couldn't stomach breakfast — very good of you, all the same, good of you all to come. Nobody here can do anything' and he turned to go — 'I'll go and feed the calves.'

'What do we make of it, neighbours?' Jimmy Warner asked.

Days later Thorpe, the postman, brought the dreaded telegram and shortly after that information that Sergeant-Major Frank Daniels, Line-regiment, lay in a field-hospital behind the battle-lines, suffering from severe wounds sustained under heavy enemy bombardment. There would be recovery in time — he was a strong man.

'At the same time as Sid, I reckon,' George said. 'I had the message for them both. Sid's dead and more than likely the sergeant's wishing he were dead too. What do you think of this dragging, wounding war that's beggaring the lot of us?'

Much later it was learned that Bombardier Sidney Norman of the Bucks Yeomanry died in the use by the enemy in Flanders of poison-gas shells and not until his wounds were healed was it known that the sergeant-major was to be invalided out with his lungs so damaged in the same action that, as Claydon miserably put it, he would never be the same man again.

He was not seen in the village again until the day of the Peace Celebrations in June, 1919, when the village hall was the scene of a Meat Tea, that is, a gargantuan and mightily testing lunch for adults, at 4.30 a tea for the children, and in the evening a Social and Dance but, before their tea, races for the children in Tompkins's Field nearby. There, a shrunken but defiantly straight and upright figure, the erstwhile sergeant-instructor acted as judge, also presenting the prizes, each winner, small or large, receiving a pat on the head and an encouraging smile.

When a voice from the crowd cried, 'The Germans couldn't bow him, could they?' there followed a general nodding and instant spontaneous clapping, at which the sergeant-major looked up surprised, for in handing a shining clasp-knife to a shy twelve-year-old winner and shaking his hand, he had not heard the observation.

At this, though, George Norman, personally much smartened for once in a while, pulling at his imperial beard, turned to go home saying, 'Well — he's got his life, if you can call it a life.'

Everyone who enjoyed Hubert Chapman's 'A Village Upbringing' published in 1979 will be glad that he has now produced a volume of short stories, all very close indeed to actuality, about the four Claydons of North Buckinghamshire, East, Botolph, Midale and Steeple Claydon, as they were in the days of his boyhood.

Hubert Chapman was born at Botolph Claydon in 1901 and became in due course a London schoolmaster, training college lecturer and much loved headmaster in the East End of London. Perhaps spending the greater part of his working life in London has thrown his early life into sharper relief. Hubert Chapman now lives in Norfolk.